SIR ISAAC NEWTON

Life of Science Library 39

Sir Isaac Newton, the portrait [by Jervas]
which he presented to the Royal Society in 1717

SIR ISAAC NEWTON

H. D. ANTHONY

Abelard-Schuman *London New York Toronto*

LONDON Abelard-Schuman Limited 38 Russell Square
NEW YORK Abelard-Schuman Limited 6 West 57 Street
TORONTO Abelard-Schuman Canada Limited 81 John Street
© *H. D. Anthony 1960*
Library of Congress Catalog Card Number 60–13040
First Published 1960

The Tercentenary of the Royal Society, celebrated in 1960, is an apt reminder of the debt which both the Society and the world of science owe to Sir Isaac Newton, President of the Society for nearly a quarter of a century.

The purpose of this study is to portray the life and work of Newton within the framework of contemporary history. Some biographers have tended to emphasise the scientific discoveries, by means of which Newton attained international fame. But so much material has become available during recent years that it is now possible to present the general reader with a more balanced account of Newton's life; for example, a good deal has lately been made known of the long period of over thirty years which he spent at the Mint. An appraisal may also be made of some at any rate of the voluminous writings in Newton's own hand, on theology and kindred subjects.

From the wealth of material available, an attempt has been made in the following pages to show the many-sided activities of one of the world's greatest men.

A glossary of words having particular meanings in British universities has been added for the benefit of American and other overseas readers.

The author is conscious of the debt he owes to the numerous writers who have contributed to the story of Newton. Their names are mentioned at appropriate places in the text. Special acknowledgment is here made to the following for permission to quote from their works:

The Hibbert Trust
  (*Newton's Theological Manuscripts*)
Sir John Craig and the Cambridge University Press
  (*Newton at the Mint*)
Professor Douglas McKie
  (a paper from the *Philosophical Magazine*)
Professor A. D. Ritchie and the Edinburgh University Press
  (*Studies in the History and Methods of the Sciences*)

Professor G. M. Trevelyan, O.M., and Messrs Methuen and
Co. Ltd.
> (*England under the Stuarts*); and the Royal Society
> (*Newton Tercentenary Celebrations*)

Professor H. W. Turnbull, F.R.S. and the Royal Society
> (*The Correspondence of Sir Isaac Newton*)

University of California Press
> (translation of Halley's ode at the beginning of the
> *Principia*)

The century into which Newton was born holds a unique position in the history of Western civilisation. In estimating the effect of the so-called "Scientific Revolution", Professor Herbert Butterfield writes:

We know now that what was emerging towards the end of the seventeenth century was a civilisation exhilaratingly new perhaps, but strange as Nineveh and Babylon. That is why, since the rise of Christianity, there is no landmark in history that is worthy to be compared with this.

Such an outstanding claim might be expected from the pen of a professional man of science; it is all the more striking as the considered judgment of the Professor of Modern History in the University of Cambridge. On what considerations then is this claim based? Why should such significant movements as the Renaissance or the Reformation, regarded as landmarks, be yet unworthy to be compared with what was taking place towards the end of the seventeenth century? The answers to these questions are to be sought in the change in mental outlook associated with the Scientific Revolution.

During the Renaissance much of the learning of the Classical period, long hidden from Western Europe, was made accessible. This wealth of information inspired interest in subjects included in the brilliant vistas of Greek thinking and Roman activity. Translations from the classics made from Arab sources stimulated knowledge of the original writers—and also an undue reverence for commentaries on their works. But the Renaissance did not involve a new mental outlook; to the majority of students, the rediscovered Aristotelian system must have appeared as reasonable as it did to their predecessors many centuries before. The Renaissance was the completion of a long process whereby the thoughts and beliefs of a forgotten age were recaptured and absorbed into the intellectual life of the time. This does not minimise the importance of the process or its value in presenting the ideals of an earlier civilisation. In the main, however, both outlook and vision were capable of assimilation in the medieval mind because they fitted into a system of the universe familiar both to the men of the fourteenth, fifteenth and sixteenth centuries and to their classical counterparts.

It is equally reasonable to establish a similar position with regard to other historical turning points. The decline of the Roman Empire, the capture of Constantinople by the Turks, the Reformation—all have far-reaching consequences; but they did not necessitate a new view of the universe, nor an apparently contradictory way of regarding the movements of the heavenly bodies.

The same cannot be said concerning the effect of the Scientific Revolution. The latter had been developing for many years —ever since certain fourteenth-century thinkers began to challenge the accepted Aristotelian ideas concerning motion. It culminated in the scientific outlook of the seventeenth century, especially that associated with Newton, and it became increasingly evident that the traditional view of the universe could no longer be held. In other words, the Scientific Revolution involved a change from views based on a static universe with the earth at its centre, to a conception in which motion played an essential role, even against the apparent evidence of the senses.

It is no small wonder that man's adjustment to this new view of his surroundings was slow. The elementary knowledge of the solar system, which forms part and parcel of our education today and which is taken for granted, makes it easy for us to under-estimate the difficulties presented to the ordinary man of the Western world at the end of the seventeenth century. The evidence of his own senses, the teaching of his Church and the general background of accepted belief around him all militated against change from the traditional view of the universe. As these difficulties were gradually overcome, so man left behind a civilisation which had held sway for many centuries, and entered one which, by contrast, may well be called modern.

The magnitude of the change and the difficulties of accepting it led to a revolution in approach to all problems of Nature. Observation and experiment were recognised as fundamental in all scientific theory. Traditional views, however venerable, were subject to scrutiny in the light of increasing knowledge. The facts concerning astronomy which had been accumulated from the earliest times, and the more systematic observations and records compiled about the end of the sixteenth century, could now be explained by the generalisations of Newton and his theory of universal gravitation, which held the key to the apparent motions of the heavenly bodies.

At a later date and in another sphere, the importance of experiment is seen in the use made of the chemical balance by Lavoisier (1743–94), at the end of the eighteenth century; this was the basis of a century of chemical achievement both in theory and in industry. In electricity, the experiments of Franklin (1706–90) in the eighteenth century and of Faraday (1791–1867), together with the mathematical work of Clerk Maxwell (1831–79) in the nineteenth, led in the present century to the discovery of the relation between electricity and matter, and to that ground common to physics and chemistry—the study of atomic structure.

The growth of geology in the nineteenth century is another illustration of the same approach to natural problems—this time leading to critical estimates of the age of the earth based on the time necessary for the formation of rocks, and the concept of the gradual evolution of living forms based on a study of fossils. At the same time the outstanding work of Charles Darwin (1809–82) with regard to natural selection was founded on a lifelong study of animal life, and patient examination of the specimens collected during the voyage of H.M.S. *Beagle*.

In the realm of medical science, the effect of the seventeenth century is equally evident. The medical works of Galen (c. A.D. 130–200) were made known through translation, and printed copies distributed throughout Europe by the end of the fifteenth century. His theories were treated with such respect that, in the words of Professor Charles Singer, " the dissection in fact was supposed to illustrate Galen, rather than Galen to explain the dissection ". Before the middle of the sixteenth century, however, there was open discussion of Galen's theories at the universities. By the seventeenth century Harvey (1578–1657) had established his belief in the circulation of the blood —and this without the evidence of direct observation which came later when Malpighi (1628–94), using a microscope, saw the passage of blood through the tiny, thin-walled vessels connecting arteries and veins, now known as blood capillaries. In view of the lack of this direct evidence, which was not available until after Harvey's death, the inferences he made from observation are all the more striking, and show to how great an extent he had broken with traditional views and with the appeal to authority, whether of Galen or Aristotle. Towards the end of the next century, Jenner (1749–1823), with careful observation and records, established the practice of vaccination against smallpox. The nineteenth century saw outstanding progress in medical science—Pasteur (1822–95), and inoculation against rabies; Lister (1827–1912), and antiseptic surgery; Simpson (1811–70), and anaesthesia, following up the work of Morton (1819–68) and other American dentists. The twentieth century has seen even more spectacular advances in medicine, surgery, and public health—all the results of observation, inference and meticulous attention to experimental detail, and in direct succession to the methods of the Scientific Revolution which culminated in the seventeenth century.

Many other examples could be given to show how scientific method has entered into modern thought and practice. Indeed claims have been put forward to include as sciences branches of study which at first sight have but little in common with the traditional subjects of the Scientific Revolution; even philosophy has taken into account the results of the new methods of approach to the problems of Nature. But the object of this prologue is not to make a complete list of the ways in which modern science has influenced human thought and achievements; it is to direct attention to the uniqueness of the seventeenth century as a landmark in history, for the new mental outlook demanded by the new ideas of the universe may be dated from then. Humanity stood on the threshold of a new era, and it was due to the genius and painstaking work of such men as Newton that the modern world has emerged, well equipped to harness the forces of Nature to the service and well being of mankind.

But the course of history has also shed a somewhat sombre light on the intellectual progress deriving from the seventeenth century. With almost unlimited possibilities for good, the loom of time has shown a strange interweaving of evil. Man is slowly and painfully realising that his knowledge of the material universe can lead to disaster, unless controlled by his faith in the values and reality of the spiritual universe. What is even of greater importance than scientific research is the way in which its results are used. This lies in the realm of the spirit. In the following pages it will be seen that, although Newton may justly be hailed as the greatest of the men of science, his interests and powers led him also beyond the apparent world of Nature to those unseen realities which cannot be expressed in the terms of mathematics or of science. With this wider interpretation of his life, the words he used towards its close are deeply significant—" the great ocean of truth lay all undiscovered before me ".

B

The year 1642, which marks the death of Galileo, may well be remembered also as the year of Newton's birth. But the inhabitants of Woolsthorpe in Lincolnshire, some six miles south of Grantham, could not have guessed that the baby born there at the manor house on Christmas Day, 1642, would become known far and wide as the world's greatest man of science.

Woolsthorpe consisted of two or three farmsteads and thatched cottages in the parish of Colsterworth, and was not well known; the family in the manor house could likewise lay no claim to special distinction. Stukeley (1687–1765), Newton's first biographer, made diligent search for records of the Newton family, and ultimately his friend, Mr. Mason, found a few vellum leaves which were the parish register of Colsterworth from 1630 to 1642. Some pages were missing and the last one disfigured, but on it under the heading " baptiz'd Anno 1642 " there appears the entry:

Isaac sonne of Isaac and Hanna Newton Jan 1

The discrepancy in the number of the year is due to the shortening of the year 1751 by nearly three months, when the Gregorian Calendar was introduced into England in 1752. Up to and including 1751, the year began on 25 March; the year 1752 began on 1 January. Thus the date 1 January, 1642, which appeared in the parish register would be reckoned as 1643 in the Gregorian Calendar. Newton's birthday, which was on 25 December, would remain as 1642.

However, the manor of Woolsthorpe has many historical associations. It probably belonged to Ulfus, the fourth son of King Harold, who was killed at the Battle of Hastings in 1066. William the Conqueror's son, William Rufus, restored the estate to Ulfus, and it is probably from the latter that the original spelling Wulsthorpe is derived. The estate reverted to the Crown at the time of Henry VIII and was probably given to Lord Burghley by Queen Elizabeth I, and sold by him or his son to John Newton, one of Sir Isaac's forebears, and it remained in the Newton family. Stukeley's description is apt—the manor

" stands in a pleasant little hollow or *convallis* on the west side of the valley of the river Witham which rises near there, one spring thereof in this hamlet of Wulsthorpe. It has a good prospect eastward, and sees the Roman road, the Hermen [Ermine] Street, going over the fields to the east of Colsterworth. There cannot be a finer country than this. The house is a pretty good one, built of white stone, which abounds all over this country." Stukeley is referring to the Jurassic limestone rocks which may be traced across England from the Dorset coast to North Yorkshire.

Newton's father, also called Isaac, was lord of the manor of Woolsthorpe. In feudal times the manor was both a unit of rural organisation and a nucleus for local government. The latter included a legal court, and at its head was the lord of the manor, everyone else on the estate being dependent on him in various ways. An interesting record of the transfer of an estate is that of Laurence Washington, mayor of Northampton and ancestor of George Washington, who purchased the property of Sulgrave manor house, near Helmdon, Northamptonshire, from King Henry VIII in 1539. There are several manor houses still in existence in England.

Isaac Newton senior had married Hannah Ayscough, and their son Isaac was born prematurely on 25 December, 1642, three months after his father's death. The health of his mother was greatly impaired by the shock of her husband's early death, so that the young Isaac started life under a twofold handicap.

The family name of Newton was derived from a town in Lancashire, while that of Ayscough came from a hamlet of that name near Bedale in Yorkshire. The Ayscoughs became a wealthy family in Lincolnshire and it was a cousin of Newton's mother, Dr. James Ayscough of Holbeach, who first inspired Stukeley to become a doctor. Stukeley developed much interest in Sir Isaac Newton and his *Memoirs* of the latter provide considerable material concerning Newton's early life, from which quotations are made from time to time in this chapter. In 1645 Mrs. Newton married a clergyman, Barnabas Smith, Rector of

North Witham, a parish south of Colsterworth and about a mile from Woolsthorpe.

An interesting and somewhat surprising account of the preliminaries attending this marriage was given to Mr. Conduitt (who married a niece of Newton) by a Mrs. Hutton, whose maiden name was Ayscough.

Mr. Smith, a neighbouring clergyman, who had a very good estate, had lived a bachelor [the parish register shows that he was a widower whose first wife died in June, 1645] till he was pretty old, and one of his parishioners advising him to marry, he said he did not know where to meet with a good wife. The man answered, the widow Newton is an extraordinary good woman. But, saith Mr. Smith, how do I know she will have me, and I don't care to ask and be denied; but if you will go and ask her, I will pay you for your day's work. He went accordingly. Her answer was, she would be advised by her brother Ayscough. Upon which Mr. Smith sent the same person to Mr. Ayscough on the same errand, who, upon consulting with his sister, treated with Mr. Smith, who gave her son Isaac a parcel of land, being one of the terms insisted upon by the widow if she married him.

The parcel of land was the nearby estate of Sustern, worth about £50 a year; this together with the paternal estate of Woolsthorpe yielded a total £80 per annum.

A tablet over the fireplace of the room where Newton was born carries the following quotation from Pope:

> Nature and nature's laws lay hid in night
> God said, Let Newton be and all was light.

These words shine with added lustre against the frailty of the puny infant destined to become one of the world's intellectual giants. At birth Newton was of such diminutive size that his mother later told him that he might have been put into a quart mug. He was also so feeble that two women who had been sent to Lady Pakenham's at North Witham for medicine did not expect to find him alive on their return. Although Newton always retained the greatest affection for his mother, it must have been a severe handicap that at the age of four he was deprived of her constant care. Mrs. Smith, as she then was, went to live with her husband the Rev. Barnabas Smith at North Witham, leaving her mother to look after the child.

The elementary education of Newton in reading, writing and arithmetic was given in two small day schools at Skillington and Stoke, about a mile from his home. Presumably this period of his life passed without incident, and it may be assumed that he took part in the social life of the time. Clearly the son of the owner of a manor house would be given some sort of preparatory instruction to enable him to take advantage of grammar school education at a later date. The "dame" school of Elizabethan times persisted in some villages until the nineteenth century. For many centuries the teacher, whether man or woman, has usually been portrayed carrying the traditional insignia of office—a small switch—for chastening! Small boys wore long coats extending almost to their ankles, for everyday wear, and an interesting account of the ceremony of "breeching" a six-year-old is contained in a seventeenth-century letter.

You cannot believe the great concerne that was in the whole family here last Wednesday, it being the day that the taylor was to helpe to dress little Frank in his breeches, in order to the making an everyday suit by it. Never had any bride that was to be drest upon her wedding night more hands about her, some the legs and some the arms, the taylor butt'ning, and others putting on the sword, and so many lookers on, that, had I not a finger amongst them I could not have seen him.

Much was expected of the housewife of those days. Gervase Markham, a soldier and authority on the English countryside who died in 1637, wrote on the title page of one of his books:

The English housewife, containing the inward and outwards vertues which ought to be in a compleat woman. As her skill in Physick, Chirurgery, Cookery, extraction of oils, banquetting stuff, ordering of great feasts, preserving of all sorts of wines, conceited secrets, distillations of perfumes, ordering of wool, hemp or flax, making cloth and dying, the knowledge of dairies, the office of malting, of oats, their excellent uses in families, of brewing, baking and all other things belonging to a household.

The institution of the carrier's cart was an aid in domestic matters, and as Woolsthorpe was only a few hundred yards from the Great North Road its appearance would be a familiar sight. The stage coach dated from about 1640, succeeding the long broad-wheeled wagons of the late sixteenth century which plied between towns with goods and passengers and were called "stages". The coach was like a large private coach and the outside passengers sat in a basket between the hind wheels. Roads were bad and highwaymen common. To deal with the hordes of beggars, each parish was authorised to issue badges to those licensed to beg. Hawkers' licences were issued, as an assurance of genuine trading, to those who tramped the countryside to sell their wares.

During Newton's boyhood, life in the small hamlet might be rather more eventful than usual, as Woolsthorpe was situated in that area of England from which Cromwell's Ironsides were drawn. The breach between Charles I and his Parliament culminated in civil war, and the King raised his standard at Nottingham in 1642. Newton's family sympathised with the Royalist cause, so the small manor house was set in the midst of a hostile region of Parliamentarian activity. Colsterworth was situated on the main road north and groups of Cromwell's men would from time to time pass along it.

So much for the homely country atmosphere of Woolsthorpe in which Newton passed his early years. The undulating nature of the ground resulted in small streams at times acquiring a considerable current. To Newton's love of the countryside would thus be added the opportunity of playing by the side of swiftly moving water and noticing its power. There is no evidence of the precocious child, but undoubtedly a bent towards things mechanical revealed itself quite early in Newton's life. When he was nine years old he carved a sundial from a block of stone and fixed it to the south wall of the manor house.

Towards the end of the nineteenth century the sundial was removed and built into the wall behind the organ at Colsterworth Church. At the age of twelve Newton was sent to the King's School at Grantham. Although the distance was only about six miles, the journey would not have been uneventful in view of what has already been written about the conditions prevailing on country roads at the time.

The old school building in which Newton was educated exists today and is used as an assembly hall for the present school. It still bears, among other initials, those of *I.N.* carved near one of the windows and the name *I. Newton* which was inscribed on one of the ledges. The old building dates back to Tudor times and is an interesting reminder of the development of the grammar school in the sixteenth century. English humanists had visited Italy and returned with a new enthusiasm for classical studies. Colet, dean of St. Paul's Cathedral, London, and Lily, the first high master of St. Paul's School, produced a Latin grammar which Henry VIII directed to be used in all grammar schools. From this period dates the traditional classical curriculum which became characteristic of both grammar schools and universities in Britain until the nineteenth century.

At school Newton does not appear to have been other than a healthy, normal and by no means perfect boy. His interest in mechanical models found practical expression out of school. During term-time he boarded with an apothecary named Clarke, whose brother was mathematical master at the school. Newton did not take a great part in games, but his leisure was fully occupied at the home of the apothecary, where doubtless his desire to test by observation and experiment was awakened. He begged a box from Mrs. Clarke's brother and made a water clock from it about four feet in height, with dial plate duly painted with figures. The wooden index which showed the hours was operated by a perpendicular piece of wood. This floated in a cistern which was gradually filled by means of water dropping regularly from a container. The latter was replenished every morning and the whole apparatus was housed in Newton's attic bedroom. Stukeley remarks that

The family upon occasion went up thither, to be well informed upon the time of day; and it was left in the house long after he [Newton] went to the University; destroyed probably when the house was pulled down and rebuilt.

Little did the young enthusiast dream that a few years later, after hearing a paper read at the Royal Society on water clocks, he would be giving the Society his own views on the accuracy and usefulness of that method of telling the time, saying:

The chief inconvenience attending it was this: the hole thro' which the water drops must necessarily be extremely small, therefore it was subject to be furr'd up by impuritys in the water. So hour-glasses made with sand will wear the hole thro' which it is transmitted bigger. These inconveniences in time spoil the use of both instruments.

Newton used all the pocket money which his mother sent for the purchase of hammers, chisels, saws and other equipment for making models. One in particular deserves special notice. The installation of a windmill near Grantham was regarded as a novelty, as the country readily lent itself to the construction of water-wheels for power. The townsfolk were accustomed to visit the site, and Newton, as well as other grammar school boys, was also interested. By watching the workmen early in the morning, Newton made a perfect model which he placed on the roof of Mr. Clarke's house, providing pieces of cloth to assist the " sails ".

But Isaac was not content with this bare imitation. . . . He put a mouse into it, which work'd it as naturally as the wind. This he used to style his mouse miller, and complained jokingly what a thief he was, for he eat up all the corn put into the mill.

There were various speculations as to how the mouse turned the mill.

However it was a piece of diversion to not a little part of the town and country, to pay a visit to Isaac's mouse miller, and the farmer readily supplyd him with handfuls of corn on Market days.

The appreciation of the populace was not, however, shared

by the teaching staff of the school. Dull boys were sometimes put above Newton in class, though he would redouble his efforts and overtake them. Then, as now, the atmosphere of " could do better " resulted in an interview with the headmaster. In Newton's case it was Henry Stokes: although his remonstrances fortunately did not lead to the abandonment of the boy's experiments, they had the desired effect.

Perhaps the story of his fight with a bully foreshadowed his dealings in later life with Judge Jeffreys. The boy concerned kicked Newton in the stomach, causing him considerable pain and aroused the latter's indignation so that he not only administered suitable physical retribution, but also determined to beat his adversary at work as well—a feat which he easily accomplished. In lighter vein Newton delighted his companions by some of his inventions—for example by making a paper lantern, and at night attaching it with lighted candle to the tail of a kite —to the consternation and fright of the uninitiated! Another incident seems to be prophetic of the man of science. On 3 September, 1658, the day of Oliver Cromwell's death, a great tempest apparently swept the country; Newton was taking part in a jumping contest, and though not ordinarily outstanding at this sport, he used his intellect to good effect; " yet observing the gusts of the wind, took so proper an advantage of them as surprisingly to outleap the rest of the boys."

When Newton was about the age of fifteen his mother found it necessary to recall him to Woolsthorpe to take charge of the family estates. Not only would his help be of value, but she wanted him to follow in the family tradition and become a yeoman farmer. But in this she was sadly disappointed, and some of the many stories of the future professor's absent-mindedness have their origin in this short interruption of his schooling. The flowing water of the rivulets of the district cast their spell upon him and diverted his attention from the ordinary duties of a farm.

But such employments ill suited with Sir Isaac's taste. When he was order'd into the field to tend on a flock of sheep, he was sitting under a tree, with a book in his hand; or busying himself with a knife, cutting models and inventions in wood. At other times he would get to a spring head or running stream, which this charming country abounds with. There he made little wheels, such as they use in water-mills, some over-shot, as they call them, some under-shot, with proper dams, sluices and many hydrostatic experiments. In the meantime the sheep under his care were stray'd into the corn field; which must occasion great outcry and damage to be paid for by his mother. Nor would Isaac so much as remember his dinner time, so intent was he in philosophical meditation.

Some of the duties for which Newton was responsible at this time necessitated his visiting Grantham. On one occasion, so it is said, he followed the usual custom of leading his horse up the steep hill out of the town towards Colsterworth, and became so engrossed in thought that instead of remounting he led the animal the remaining five miles home. And so do such legends of the great multiply that it is said that on another occasion the horse slipped his bridle and went off home, while Newton walked on bridle in hand never having missed his steed. Thus did Newton conform to the traditional notion that genius and absent-mindedness are related.

The late George Bernard Shaw has woven a story similar to these in the play, *In Good King Charles's Golden Days*, first produced at the Malvern Festival in August, 1939. The opening scene portrays George Fox, the Quaker, calling on Isaac Newton at Cambridge in the year 1680. Mrs. Basham, Newton's house-keeper, is asking her master's help ". . . since you have one of your calculating fits on I wonder would you mind doing a little sum for me to check the washing bill. How much is three times seven?" Mrs. Basham explains that at school she got as far as addition and subtraction, but could never do multiplication or division. Newton replies they are quite unnecessary as you can add the logarithms of the numbers and look up the antiloga-rithm of their sum. By this means he gives the result of multiply-ing three by seven as less than 22 and more than 20. When a tradesman instantly gives the answer, 21, Shaw makes Newton say, "Extraordinary! Here was I blundering over this simple problem for a whole minute; and this uneducated fish-hawker solves it in a flash! He is a better mathematician than I."

It is fortunate for the world that Newton's headmaster had become rector of Colsterworth when the former had left school and so could attempt to influence Mrs. Smith to allow her son to return to Grantham. At length Stokes prevailed, adding that he would " make a compliment to her of the 40s. per annum paid to the schoolmaster by all foreign lads ". Stukeley presumably means by " foreign " those boys whose homes were outside Grantham. He also allowed Newton to board at the headmaster's house. One can imagine the concentrated coaching and inter-play of personality as the scholar of experience prepared the youth of promise for entry to the University of Cambridge. Per-haps Stokes realised that the task was not an ordinary one, and that the head boy of the small world of the grammar school might perchance rise high in the larger realm of the University. At any rate the bond between master and pupil went deeper than that of superficial learning, for when the day came in 1661 for Newton at the age of eighteen to leave the platform of school attainment to climb the ladder of university achievement, his old headmaster " with the pride of a father, placed his favourite pupil in the most conspicuous part of the school, and having, with tears in his eyes, made a speech in praise of his character and talents, held him up to the scholars as a proper object of their love and admiration ".

There have been a few periods in the history of civilisation more significant and transitional than the one in which Newton lived. Indeed, in the history of science, what may well be termed the Newtonian Age represents the culmination of the scientific revolution, and heralds the advance of all branches of science from the seventeenth to the twentieth centuries.

Sir Richard Livingstone, in one of his books on education, likened men's achievement through the long years of history to the climbing of a three-stranded rope representing action, knowledge and vision. Just as in a rope the strands are interwoven, so these three aspects of human nature are interdependent. They do, however, form a useful background against which a survey may be made of any period of history. In undertaking such a survey, it must be remembered that there is no clear-cut division between action, knowledge and vision, any more than there is between such periods of history as classical, medieval and modern. Nor in the life of one individual are there marked boundaries, though there may be a tendency to speak of him as a man of action, or of knowledge, or of vision, if one or other of these attributes seems to predominate.

The traditional estimate of Newton rightly emphasises the contribution he made to our knowledge of the material universe; but that part of his life, extending over thirty years, as a man of action in national affairs, has sometimes been overlooked. Further, his concern for matters of the spirit, his vision, has only comparatively recently been brought to public notice in the mass of his theological writings. In view of these varied interests and his response to the political, intellectual, religious and philosophical atmosphere of the day, it may be of value, at this point, to give some account of contemporary background in the life and thought of Newton's generation.

So far as the story of Europe in the seventeenth century is concerned, it is not easy to disentangle the complex interaction of political and religious history. The loyalties aroused by Reformation and Counter-Reformation were reflected in the political atmosphere of the time. To appreciate this atmosphere it is essential to have some idea of the long and tortuous path, extending over hundreds of years, which led to the European scene of the seventeenth century.

The pattern of life within the Roman Empire lingered in men's minds long after the incursions of Teutonic peoples into Roman territory during the fourth and fifth centuries. In the following century Slavonic influence became dominant in Eastern Europe, and in the seventh century the Arab-Islam infiltration involved almost all the seaboard of the Mediterranean. From the eighth to the tenth centuries Vikings from Scandinavia harassed Britain and other coasts of North-west Europe. There were thus three successors to the united Mediterranean of Roman times: the Eastern or Byzantine Empire; the Islamic lands, and Western Europe. The continuity of civilisation within the first two of these areas was in marked contrast to the lack of cohesion of the third.

For the present purpose special attention is directed to the divisions of Europe and the desire, which can be discerned from time to time, to re-establish the unifying tradition of the Roman Empire. By the sixteenth century the Hapsburg Emperor Charles V aspired to become the lay leader of a united Christendom. The ambition was never realised and the struggle of France against the Empire provides the background of the wars of the seventeenth century. Indeed, the Reformation also must be seen within the framework of France's conflict with the Holy Roman Empire.

In the light of this conflict for supremacy in Europe, the earlier view, that the Thirty Years War was essentially a contest between Protestants and Roman Catholics, now requires considerable modification. The accepted dates (1618–48) do not include the unrest which preceded and followed them. The devastation was less than has popularly been believed. During much of this time the economic and cultural background of Germany was improving from its position at the end of the sixteenth century. At this point some reference must be made to the baroque influence which was so characteristic of the period.

In his book *The Age of the Baroque 1610–1660* (1952), Professor Carl J. Friedrich of Harvard University seeks to unify the approach to the study of the seventeenth century. He shows how the main trends in religion and philosophy, politics and economics, music and science are the expressions of a prevailing state of mind—the baroque. Like the term gothic in architecture, baroque was originally a term of opprobrium and Professor Friedrich dates the baroque style from the middle of the sixteenth to the middle of the eighteenth century, culminating in the region of 1760. Within this period and for an appreciable part of it Newton lived, and the scientific revolution reached its climax. The broader view which draws together the movements of the seventeenth century as an expression of one attitude of mind stands in contrast to a narrow appreciation of political and military events in association with religious conflict.

In France, the reign of Louis XIV from 1661 to his death in 1715 was contemporary with almost the whole of Newton's professional career, whether considered from the point of view of his academic studies at Cambridge, or his national responsibilities as Master of the Mint in London. The long reign of Louis XIV inaugurated for France a period of security from foreign attack and freedom from serious civil disorder, which lasted until the Revolution of 1789. The political complications of the Thirty Years War involving the Bourbons of France and the Hapsburgs of Spain are clearly beyond the scope of this survey. It is sufficient to point out here that the first part of the contest was completed by the Treaty of Westphalia (1648), and the second by the Treaty of the Pyrenees (1659), each of which brought an unstable peace to the Continent. Nor can details be given of the diplomacy which preceded the Treaties of Ryswich (1697) ending the War of the Grand Alliance, which had involved William III of England. The death of Charles II of Spain in 1700 made possible the European conflagration known as the War of the Spanish Succession (1701–1712) in which the Duke of Marlborough led the English forces and played so important a part.

The results of political affairs in England may be more familiar. The change from Tudors to Stuarts, following the death of Queen Elizabeth I in 1603; the theory of the Divine Right of Kings, culminating in the clash between the King and Parliament, and the beheading of Charles I in 1649; the rise of Oliver Cromwell, the Civil War, and then the Restoration of Charles II to the throne in 1660—all these are forerunners of that brilliant scientific age of which the Royal Society, founded in 1660, is so significant.

Later came the Glorious Revolution of 1689 which placed William and Mary from Holland on the throne; it was preceded by the flight of James II (who had succeeded his brother Charles II) to France whither his wife and infant son had already gone —none of them ever to return.

The "glory" of this revolution lay, not only in the lack of violence which preceded its success, but above all in the pattern of settlement which future generations of Englishmen could follow. In this way a second civil war was avoided, and the way made clear for disputes to be disposed of without bloodshed. Undoubtedly Louis XIV of France did not expect such a peaceful outcome, otherwise he would have prevented his rival, William of Orange, from setting sail from Holland to ascend the throne of England with his consort Mary. The latter, who was the eldest child of James II, had married William, Prince of Orange in 1677, but in 1689 she declined to rule as sole sovereign —hence the joint title, William III and Mary II.

The Convention Parliament of which Newton was a member assembled in 1689 and played an important part in healing the wounds of an earlier age. Not much more than a generation before, Roundheads (Parliamentarians) and Cavaliers (Royalists) were taking sides in the Civil War which resulted in the execution of Charles I in 1649. Before this, Anglican and Puritan had been engaged in such bitter controversy that during the persecution instigated by Archbishop Laud some twenty thousand Englishmen had migrated to New England over the years 1628–1640. Thither they had been preceded by their fellow-countrymen, the Pilgrim Fathers, in 1620 who, in their turn, had also fled from the intolerant religious atmosphere of their own country. This historical background of political and reli-

c

gious upheaval was followed by an atmosphere of national unity, as shown by the Convention Parliament, such as could not have been attained during the preceding years of the seventeenth century.

Only four years before the Convention Parliament had been convened, the Duke of Monmouth, whose claim to the throne had been supported by the Whigs and who had fled to Holland when these supporters were arrested, landed at Lyme Regis with a few followers. Monmouth gained the support of the peasants of Dorset and Somerset and of the persecuted Puritan inhabitants of Taunton, but he was defeated at Sedgemoor (1685). The bloodshed of the battlefield found its counterpart after the battle in the Bloody Assize of Judge Jeffreys, when James II allowed three hundred of the peasants to be hanged.

In contrast to this internal conflict stands the "glory" of the Revolution of 1689. Both Whig and Tory finally rose together against the autocratic rule of the Roman Catholic James II and, after the coming of the Protestant William and Mary to England, agreed on the Revolution Settlement, under which England has lived at peace within herself to the present day.

Through this period of transition lived Newton, taking his seat as a representative of the University of Cambridge in the Convention Parliament. His sympathies were Whig rather than Tory, and it may be fitting to close this brief account of English political development in the seventeenth century by a short reference to the origin of the two terms. In December 1679 began a series of petitions to Charles II, who had ruled without a Parliament for some years, to bring pressure on him to call the elected Parliament together. Sentiment on the other side abhorred this conduct, so that in the following February counter-addresses of "abhorrence" reached the King. Thus grew up the terms "Petitioners" and "Abhorrers", which during 1680 were changed for those of "Whig" and "Tory". The change is associated with the infamous Titus Oates and the imaginary Roman Catholic plot against the Protestants and the King, details of which he circulated in 1678.

Although Charles II treated the story with contempt, Oates swore to its truth before a magistrate, Sir Edmund Berry Godfrey, who was later found dead in a ditch. During the excitement caused by this incident, which was believed to give credence to the story of the plot, Oates was accustomed to cry "Tory" at any man who dared to doubt his word. The name Tory was probably derived from Irish Roman Catholic bandits who waylaid Saxon settlers. Such an epithet called forth from the opposite side the term "Whig", which had been applied to both rebels and Scottish Covenanters, and so could suggest opposition to an established authority. Tory and Whig were associated with current opposing views and in these names may be traced the origin of the two-party system which is characteristic of present-day Parliamentary procedure in Britain.

The Whig party had two main objects, namely, to wrest political power from the Crown and to force the squirearchy and bishops to grant toleration to dissent. It will be seen later that, as the story of his life unfolds, and as he was confronted with the arbitrary attitude of the Roman Catholic James II, Newton's sense of freedom led to his supporting the Whigs in the Parliament to which he was elected in 1689.

In addition to the many alterations in the political scene Newton must have witnessed, there were several indications of the coming social changes which had their origin during his lifetime. The problems of population may be recognised in 1661 in John Graunt's *London Bills of Mortality*. It was Marshal Vauban, the French military engineer, who first realised the value of such vital statistics. The improvement in instruments of precision introduced a new approach in the general atmosphere of business life; the English excelled in the art of making mathematical instruments. Although the Dutch had introduced many of their crafts, it is of interest to note that when the elder brother of Christian Huygens (who had made watches possible by the invention of the balance-spring) came to live in London as the secretary of William III, it is recorded that he was often in and out of the clockmakers' shops. It is easy to accept, as a matter of course, the modern world's dependence on accurate timekeepers, but it is not always realised that the perfection of the clock as an accurate time-measurer was a necessary prelude to ascertaining position at sea. The provision of light-houses (the Eddystone, off Plymouth, was finished in 1699), of buoys, diving bells, harbours, canals made communication by water safer. Industry was introducing little-known processes. There were corks for bottles, paving stones and some form of lighting for streets. Sawmills were introduced into England in 1663, but then abandoned because of opposition.

Changes were taking place in constitutional history: the attributes of sovereignty were increasingly evident. The function of monarchy in the seventeenth century has been described by Sir George Clarke " as the substitution of a simpler and more unified government for the complexities of feudalism ". Armies became the normal possession of a state in time of peace as well as in war. The New Model Army of Cromwell formed the traditional background of military evolution in Britain. Navies took their place, especially after the defeat of the Armada, as essential in the active defence of the interests of a maritime power. The science of fortifications came into its own, especially so in the hands of the great military engineer, Marshal Vauban (1633–1707) who protected France with a network of fortresses, one of which, Belfort, endured a three months siege as late as 1870–71, during the Franco-Prussian War.

The Dutch scholar Grotius (1583–1645) built up a firm system of international jurisprudence. From the conception of states, frontiers and colonies, political thought developed as a consequence of growing national consciousness. The *Areopagitica* of Milton in 1644 was not an appeal against the authority of the state, in relation to a competing authority, but an appeal for freedom.

In the realm of the intellect the fruits of the Renaissance had spread westwards from Italy, which had been the home of the revival of learning. Few could foresee the mental upheaval of the scientific revolution that was to come about through the labours of Copernicus, Tycho Brahe, Kepler, Galileo and above all Newton. Nor could one anticipate the change in the approach to problems of health and disease that would result from the work of Harvey and his predecessors. Francis Bacon (1561–1626), with his insistence on experiment and actual recording of the result, must have inspired the group of keen amateurs whose scientific discussions were interrupted by the outbreak of the Civil War in 1642. There is a certain irony attaching to Bacon's desire for experiment, inasmuch as his death was caused by a cold which he caught while stuffing a fowl with snow near Highgate, then a village to the north of London, with the object of observing the effect of cold on the preservation of flesh.

The so-called Invisible College, and later its successor, the Royal Society, were symbols of the new approach to Nature, and it was through the Royal Society that Newton's discoveries were made known. The brilliant band of experimenters associated with the Royal Society in England, the Paris Academy of Sciences and the corresponding body in Italy, laid the foundations of modern science. From the natural philosophy of those days there sprang the ever-widening network of individual sciences in the eighteenth and nineteenth centuries.

Well has the seventeenth been described as the "century of genius": A. N. Whitehead in *Science and the Modern World* (1926) has aptly described its significance. He points out that the European races during the succeeding two centuries have been living upon the accumulated capital of ideas which the genius of the seventeenth century provided. This followed the revolt of the sixteenth century against accepted tradition, and those who directed this new approach handed on systems of thought which have affected every facet of our lives. It is fortunate that the century provided outstanding men of genius who were equal to the opportunities presented. Whitehead directs attention to the variety of its literary achievement. The crowded stage of this hundred years is indicated by the coincidences which mark its literary annals. At its dawn Bacon's *Advancement of Learning* and Cervantes' *Don Quixote* were published in the same year (1605), as though the epoch would introduce itself with a forward and a backward glance. The first quarto edition of *Hamlet* appeared in the preceding year, and a slightly variant edition in the same year. Finally Shakespeare and Cervantes died on the same day, April 23, 1616. In the spring of this same year Harvey is believed to have first expounded his theory of the circulation of the blood in a course of lectures before the College of Physicians in London. Newton was born in the year that Galileo died (1642), exactly one hundred years after the publication of Copernicus' *De Revolutionibus*.

One consequence of the Reformation in England is sometimes overlooked. When Henry VIII suppressed the lesser and greater monasteries in the years 1536 and 1539 respectively, a special problem was presented to the musicians of the Anglican Church. The former music of the Roman Church, which had been composed for Latin sentences, was not suitable for the First English Prayer Book of 1549. The English Church musicians of the mid-sixteenth century met the new demands with marked success and contributed to the fame of the first Elizabethan Age. After various modifications the Prayer Book, as known today, was sanctioned in May 1662 by the Restoration Act of Uniformity; it was ordered to be used with effect from the following Christmas Day. At this time Newton had entered his second year at Cambridge and could not fail to have been influenced by current religious events. As long before as 1539 Archbishop Cranmer by the publication of "the Great Bible" met the public demand that the scriptures should be available in English. The Prayer Book further enhanced the value of the native tongue. It is interesting to note that during Newton's lifetime English was replacing Latin as the language of learning. Newton's *Principia* was written in Latin and published in 1687, whereas the first edition of the *Opticks* appeared in English in 1703. Earlier, Descartes published his *Meditationes* and two years later his *Principia Philosophiae*. As Whitehead points out, there simply was not time for the century to space out nicely its notable events concerning men of genius.

No survey of the seventeenth century can be complete without reference to the religious and philosophical movements of the time. Here, though such references must inevitably be brief, it should not be forgotten that both religion and philosophy formed an important background to Newton's life, first at Cambridge and later in London. Indeed in the box which he packed and locked when he left Cambridge to take up his duties at the Mint in 1696 there were manuscripts containing over a million and a quarter words on theological subjects. This aspect of Newton's studies will be discussed in Chapter X.

The religious life of Europe was affected by the Reformation. From the time when, in 1520, Martin Luther publicly burnt the Papal Bull of Excommunication, a movement was set on foot which challenged the authority of the Roman Church, and in so doing tended to transfer that authority to the Bible. By the dawn of the seventeenth century the Reformed Churches had accepted the principles of the Reformation, and separated from the Church of Rome. In England the recently established Anglican Church had still to face the bitterness of those who clung to the older traditional Roman beliefs. From the citadel of the Anglican Church itself, however, there were those who carried the zeal of persecution into their treatment of any who would not "conform".

The Puritan Party had hopes of reforming the Church from within; but the "Separatists" had given up such hopes and had founded a Separatist Church. Within the walls of the old manor house of Scrooby in 1606, Richard Clyfton, the former rector of nearby Babworth, was the first minister: he had been deprived of his living because the simplicity of his religious convictions was not acceptable to his ecclesiastical superiors. Among the members of the Separatist congregation was William Bradford, later Governor of the New Plymouth Colony. Scrooby is situated on the Great North Road, not many miles from Grantham where Newton was at school. Local informers and government spies travelling north brought the meetings at Scrooby manor to the notice of the Bishop of Lincoln and the Archbishop of York. As Sovereign, Church and State were at this time regarded as a unity, it was not likely that such "separatism" would be tolerated, and Bradford describes the resulting

persecution thus: ". . . some were taken and clapt up in
prison, others had their houses beset and watched day and night
. . . and most were fain to fly and leave their houses and habi-
tation and their means of livelyhood."

Reference may be made now to another Separatist, partly
because of the influence that Cambridge had on him, and partly
for the part he played in the project of the *Mayflower*. William
Brewster (*c.* 1566–1644) (not to be confused with Sir David
Brewster, the nineteenth-century biographer of Newton), who
entered Peterhouse, Cambridge, in 1580, was attracted by the
teaching of certain radical scholars and preachers in the University. These defied authority and advocated reform in the conduct of public worship and greater freedom for the individual
in the interpretation of the Scriptures. Brewster later went on
a diplomatic mission to Holland, but his service at the court of
Elizabeth I came to an end when his chief, Sir William Davison,
was made a scapegoat for the execution of Mary Queen of Scots
in 1587. Thereafter Brewster became Master of the Queen's
Post at Scrooby—an office which made him responsible for the
relays of horses on the post road. On this road were the "post-
stages" or stopping places to which the Queen's packet or mail
was carried from the previous "stage" and whence it was con-
veyed to the next. Brewster's father previously held the position,
and his son, for a short time, had assisted him. Brewster was
greatly influenced by Clyfton and also by another Cambridge
scholar, John Smyth, who had organised an independent or
Separatist Church at Gainsborough about twelve miles from
Scrooby in 1602. By 1607 Brewster had resigned his post, probably under pressure, and was soon ordered to appear at York,
where he was fined the not inconsiderable sum of twenty pounds
for "being disobedient in matters of religion". He was more
fortunate than his Cambridge friend John Penry, and other
contemporaries, who had been imprisoned in the Fleet, a
London prison near the present Fleet Street, and sent to the
gallows on similar charges. Enough has been written to indicate the restless spirit of freedom which was revealing itself at
Cambridge by the beginning of the seventeenth century—a

freedom that Newton defended before the end of the century against no less a prerogative than that of James II.

The price of freedom in religious matters which Brewster and his friends decided to pay was that of voluntary exile abroad. The knowledge that in Holland such freedom could be exercised freely decided them on the choice of that country. The story of the ultimate course of the Pilgrim Fathers is sufficiently well known to mention only a few of the landmarks.

After one abortive attempt to leave for Holland, the women and children were sent by water along the River Trent, a tributary of the River Humber, to Killingholme Creek—now the site of Immingham Dock, near the estuary of the Humber. Here they were joined by their men folk who had walked overland— a distance of some thirty-five miles from Gainsborough. After a perilous voyage they established themselves at Amsterdam and ultimately Leyden, where they founded the Pilgrim Press. Deciding that their ultimate destination was to be the New World, an approach was made to James I (who some fifteen years earlier had threatened " I will make them conform, or harry them out of the land ") who agreed not to hinder the enterprise, particularly as it promised further colonisation. The *Mayflower*, which had been chartered for the voyage, put into Plymouth and the Pilgrims enjoyed the hospitality of that city. They were so conscious of the kindness and hospitality which met them on every hand during their fortnight's stay in Plymouth that when they ultimately reached the New World the Pilgrims named the spot "The Plimouth Plantation", and the rock on which they landed "Plimoth Rock", in honour of the city. They sailed from the Barbican, which is now a district adjoining Sutton Pool; originally it denoted the gateway to the castle, built for defence on the slopes of the Hoe, above the harbour; later it was used for the quay and fish market below. The Barbican is historic: it was the point of departure and return of Drake, the first Englishman to encircle the globe. Beside the stone commemorating the departure of the *Mayflower* on 6 September, 1620, is another directing attention to the fact that the American airmen who made the first Trans-Atlantic flight, set foot at the same spot, 31 May, 1919—a happy link between the Old World and the New. It is interesting comment on the spirit of freedom which was the mainspring of the first *Mayflower* expedition that her replica, *Mayflower II*, built at near-by Brixham, made her voyage in the summer of 1957 as evidence of the friendly co-operation between the English-speaking peoples on either side of the Atlantic. The spirit of independence of the Pilgrim Fathers had been fostered by the teaching and preaching of a group of Cambridge men at the end of the sixteenth century. By the middle of the seventeenth, another group flourished—the Cambridge Platonists—and counted among their number Henry More, of Christ's College. More was a native of Grantham, and Clarke, the mathematical master at the King's School, was one of his pupils. How natural therefore was the bond of friendship that was forged at Cambridge between Newton and More, and how inevitable the influence of the latter, both in matters of religion and of philosophy.

To understand the place of philosophical thought in the seventeenth century it is necessary to appreciate the fundamental part previously played by scholastic philosophy. This also has an important bearing on the general attitude displayed towards the Scientific Revolution. Any short statement of the views held by the schoolmen is liable to suffer from the distortion arising from oversimplification. It is, however, fair to claim that the fabric of Christian theology had been so closely knit with Aristotelian conceptions that any attack on the latter was regarded as a challenge to the whole Christian faith.

The decline of Aristotle's authority is one of the features of seventeenth-century philosophy, and may be seen in the changing attitude of the Roman Church. In 1632 the theory of tides which Galileo had put forward was condemned by a special congregation of the Vatican for the following reasons: (1) he misjudges his opponents, and especially those writers such as Aristotle whose views are most in conformity with those of the Church; (2) he maintains an equality of human and divine intelligence, especially in the comprehension of geometric things; (3) he deduces the ebb and flow of the sea, which exist, from the immobility of the sun and the movement of the earth, which do not exist.

These reasons in their different ways illustrate the unparalleled change in mental outlook that would be necessary in the light of the Scientific Revolution which was already dawning. At the beginning of the century, in 1616, the Copernican system was officially condemned; a little later, Kepler's works were placed on the *Index Librorum Prohibitorum*, but by 1634 no more books supporting Copernicus were prohibited. The work of Copernicus however was not taken off the *Index* until 1835.

The breakaway from the Scholastic tradition and approach was first made complete by Descartes, and in this respect he is regarded as the founder of modern philosophy. At the time of Newton, Descartes' views dominated both the philosophical and scientific outlook, especially on the continent of Europe. Newton made careful study of the mathematical and scientific writings of Descartes. In typical language Sir David Brewster writes, " Thus entrenched as the Cartesian system was, in the strongholds of the human mind, and fortified by its most obstinate prejudices, it was not to be wondered at that the pure and sublime doctrines of the *Principia* were distrustfully received, and perseveringly resisted." Mention of the names of some of the philosophers of the period—Spinoza, Hobbes, Pascal, Leibniz, Locke—is sufficient indication of the change taking place. The constructive approach, so characteristic of the seventeenth century philosophers, had released European thought from the limitations of authoritative scholasticism and of " imitative humanism ". It is not surprising therefore that these philosophers prepared the way for the speculative work of the eighteenth century and led men to question the principles underlying the general organisation of society known as the " Ancien Régime ". The philosophical revolution had preceded the political, and as has often happened in the history of human thought, the lead was really not given by statesmen but by the thinkers.

The brief survey of contemporary background contained in this chapter has revealed something of the complexity of

Western civilisation at that time. Equally apparent is the transitional nature of the period. But Newton was then at the threshold of manhood, and he could have had little conception of the outstanding part he was destined to play in the changing scene.

Cambridge has had a long history as a centre of learning; and by the time that Newton became an undergraduate its University had seen many changes and vicissitudes. Whether as "Camboritum" of Roman days, "Grantebrycgr" of the Anglo-Saxon Chronicle; or "Grentebrige" of Domesday, the place must have been of considerable importance. Two great Roman roads—Akeman Street, running east and west and the Via Devana north and south—met at Cambridge, which was confined at first to the rising ground on the northern bank of the river Cam. Here William the Conqueror built a castle, and under its walls a Norman sheriff founded the Church of St. Giles, associating with it a small body of secular canons. The latter were neither monks, friars nor parish priests, but their duties included instruction of the community in which they lived. It is reasonable therefore to assume that, in the twelfth century, educational work was already being carried on, and this may have formed the nucleus which afterwards developed into the university.

On the continent of Europe during the twelfth century, there could be seen groups of students, from boys to older men, travelling from one centre of learning to another. From the "Universitas", or guild formed by the students, has come our modern word "University", its usage resulting from the evolution of two processes—the recognition of teachers or masters on the one hand, and the organisation of students on the other. By the end of the thirteenth century Cambridge possessed an organised body of teachers, and the collegiate system had been introduced by the founding of the University's oldest College, Peterhouse or St. Peter's College. This system helped in maintaining order and discipline among the students, and by the end of the fourteenth century some seven foundations had been established; the fifteenth century saw the founding of King's, Queens', St. Catherine's and Jesus Colleges.

The Renaissance influenced the development of Cambridge in the sixteenth century; though the sojourn of Erasmus at Queens' College at the beginning of the century was resented. The light which he had kindled was not however extinguished, for through his teaching the way was prepared for the Reformation. Although there was apprehension as to whether the Colleges would be suppressed, like the religious orders, in that upheaval, they emerged with their position strengthened. In fact, in 1546, royal letters were granted for the foundation of a college of literature, the sciences, philosophy, good arts and sacred theology, consisting of one master and sixty fellows and scholars, to be called "Trynitie College, within the towne and universitie of Cambridge, of Kynge Henry the Eights foundacion". The College included Michaelhouse, which had been founded soon after Peterhouse, so that Trinity may, in a manner, contest with the latter the claim to represent the earliest example of College discipline. Trinity College is an outstanding example of the change from medieval to modern, and from Roman Catholic to Protestant, ideas of education and learning.

Religious and political fervour swayed the University during the next few decades, reflecting the temper of the country on these matters. Although the Restoration in 1660 found most of the colleges at a low ebb, it heralded a period of considerable intellectual activity. Two important movements may be discerned, one in the realm of theology and the other in natural philosophy. The former was led by such divines as Ralph Cudworth (1617–88) and Henry More (1614–87), who were greatly influenced by the philosophy of Descartes (1596–1650). They sought to prove that religion and philosophy were perfectly reconcilable, much like the Christian Platonists of the second and third centuries. The leaders of this movement have since been known as "Cambridge Platonists", and some idea of their popularity may be gauged from the comment of a leading London bookseller who declared that for twenty years after the return of Charles II (who reigned from 1660 until 1685), More's works "ruled all the booksellers in London".

The second movement, though not as publicised in its early years, was more permanent in its results, and if Newton was influenced by the atmosphere of Cambridge Platonism around him, he was, without doubt, the outstanding contributor to the movement in natural philosophy. In 1639, Horrocks (c. 1619–41)

47

of Emmanuel College had supported the Copernican theory, and had watched the transit of Venus. By the middle of the century William Oughtred (1575–1660), a Fellow of King's, Seth Ward (1617–89), a Fellow of Sidney Sussex and Wallis (1616–1703), a Fellow of Queens', were avowed Copernicans; the last two became Savilian professors at Oxford. Within two years of Newton's arrival at Cambridge, Isaac Barrow (1630–77), a Fellow of Trinity, was appointed the first Lucasian professor of mathematics, a chair which had been founded in 1663 by Henry Lucas. After five years Barrow resigned in favour of Newton, who held the professorship for over thirty years, becoming not only the most brilliant of the mathematical sons of his "alma mater", but also the doyen of the world of science.

But we are anticipating the course of events. The two movements to which reference has been made were gaining ground when Newton left King's School, Grantham, to go into residence at Cambridge; their leaders were well known in the University. Even during his undergraduate days, Newton would be subject to their influences; and later much more so as a Fellow of Trinity, for his status would allow more direct contact, both within and outside his own College.

With regard to the actual fabric of the College, it is not difficult for anyone familiar with the Cambridge of today to visualise the general appearance of Trinity at the time of Newton. Fortunately engravings and surveys made in the seventeenth century enable an accurate picture to be drawn. The Great Court was completed in 1605, and this, with the Great Gate, forms one of the best-known features of the College. The dimensions of the former, 334 feet by 228 feet, give meaning to the legendary college feat of running round its perimeter of nearly a quarter of a mile in record time before breakfast! The foundation of Trinity College seems to be due to King Henry VIII's wish not to be outshone by Wolsey. The Great Court was deliberately designed to be larger than that belonging to the Cardinal's College, Christ Church, Oxford. The only part of the Great Court which has been seriously altered since Newton's day is the south-west corner, which was rebuilt in 1770. This

The Mannor house of Wulfthorp in the parish
of Colsterworth Lincolnshire, where Sr Isaac
Newton was born: being his own estate.

Woolsthorpe Manor as it appears in
Stukeley's *Memoirs of the Life of Sir Isaac Newton*

Drills, Gravers, a Hone & Hammer & a mandrill 0 . 5 . 0
A Magnet _____ 0 . 16 . 0
Compasses _____ 0 . 3 . 6
Glass bubbles _____ 0 . 4 . 0
Chappell Clarke _____ 0 . 2 . 6
My Bachelors Cloak _____ 0 . 17 . 6
At ye Taverne severall other times &c } 1 . 0 . 0
Spent on my Cozen Ayscough 0 . 12 . 6
On other Acquaintance _____ 0 . 10 . 0
Shoos _____ 0 . 4 . 0
Cloth 2 yards & Buckles for a Vest 2 . 0 . 0
for Woosted Prunella gr{a} 1½ . 1 . 5 . 6
for ye lining 4 y{ds} _____ 0 . 9 . 4
Philosophicall Intelligences _____ 0 . 9 . 0
ye Hystory of ye Royall Soc: 0 . 7 . 0
Shoo Strings _____ 0 . 3 . 0
To Goodwife Powell _____ 0 . 7 . 6
To my Laundresse _____ 0 . 8 . 6
To Caverly : _____ 0 . 1 . 6
To the Glasier _____ 0 . 1 . 9
new fire shels & pointing } 0 . 1 . 6
chamber & windows _____
Gunters book & sector to D{s} Stokes 0 . 5 . 0
Letters, wyer, files, boals, _____ 0 . 2 . 6
for a Hellows key _____ 0 . 1 . 0
To tape twining _____
To the Taylor Octob 29 . 1667 2 . 13 . 0
To the Taylor June 10 . 1667 _____ 1 . 3 . 10
For keeping Christmas _____ 0 . 5 . 0
Lost at cards at twist _____ 0 . 15 . 0

At ye Taverne twice _____ 0 . 3 . 6
6½ sacks of coales, carriage & sedge } 0 . 11 . 0
_____ 0 . 4 . 10
Shoos & mending _____ 0 . 5 . 0
Two paire of Gloves _____ 0 . 5 . 0
Whitn{e} Lusmore, Hawtry, Salter . 0 . 3 . 6
_____ 0 . 10 . 0
Received of my Tutor & of Cousin Perkins } 0 . 10 . 0

Jo went into ye Country
December 4th 1667 .
& returned to Cambridge
Feb 12 . 1667 .
Received of my Mother _____ 30 . 0 . 0
My Journey _____ 0 . 7 . 6
for my degree to ye Colledg 5 . 10 . 0
To ye Proctor _____ 2 . 0 . 0
for 3 Prismes _____ 0 . 3 . 0
4 ounces of Putty _____ 0 . 1 . 4
To ye Painter _____ 0 . 3 . 0
To ye Joyner _____ 1 . 1 . 8
Lent to D{s} Wickins X 1 . 7 . 6
To ye shoe maker _____ 0 . 5 . 0
Bacons Miscelanys _____ 0 . 1 . 6
Expences caused by my Degree 0 . 15 . 0

Personal accounts for 1667, from a notebook probably preserved by
Newton as evidence of the priority of some of his researches contained therein

involved the demolition of the old Hall of Michaelhouse, but as the corner is partially screened from the north-east by the Fountain in the centre, the view of the court from the rooms which Newton occupied as a Fellow, between the Great Gate and the Chapel, was very similar to that of the present time. It may not be inappropriate here to quote the summary of Newton's record at Trinity as it appears in Volume II of *Admissions to Trinity College, Cambridge:*

Newton, Isaac: afterwards Knighted. Subsizar June 5, 1661. Tutor Mr. Pulleyn (matriculated 1661, Scholar 1664; B.A. 1664–5; Fellow 1667; M.A., 1668. Tutor 1669–1687. Lucasian Professor of Mathematics 1669–1702. Member of Parliament for the University 1689 and 1701).

Brief though the record is, it is substantially longer than the great majority of contemporary entries.

The mention in every entry in the *Admissions* of the tutor is a reminder of the very early introduction of this office. Before 1276 the student seems to have been under no supervision whatsoever, and though this might be regarded by present-day undergraduates as Utopian, a decree was issued by the University in that year forbidding anyone to receive a scholar unless such scholar "had a fixed master within 15 days after his entry into the university". Many of the resident Fellows acted as tutors, some having only one or two pupils and, at the time of Newton, in addition to being *in loco parentis* to their pupils, the tutors also instructed them. In Newton's first year, forty-one freshmen matriculated (compared with some 260 at present); his tutor Mr. Pulleyn, a Leicestershire man, eleven years older than his charge, subsequently became professor of Greek in the University. It was, however, through Isaac Barrow that Newton was introduced to current mathematical knowledge. Between 1669 and 1687 Newton held the position of tutor. Among the Portsmouth papers in the University Library at Cambridge is a memorandum by Newton on the studies and discipline of the University; it begins: "Undergraduates to be instructed by a Tutor, a Humanity Lecturer, a Greek Lecturer, a Philosophy

Lecturer, and a Mathematic Lecturer." There is a human touch, and perhaps a vein of humour in the extract: "Fasting nights have a shadow of religion without any substance. 'Tis only supping more pleasantly out of the public hall." The final paragraph may have been prompted by Newton's love of freedom. "No oaths of office to be imposed on the Lecturers. I do not know a greater abuse of religion than that sort of oaths. . . . Admonitions and pecuniary mulcts for neglect of duty are less cruel punishments than the consequence of perjury, and may be as effectual."

The normal undergraduate course of study at the middle of the seventeenth century consisted of classics, logic and a little elementary mathematics. The study of Euclid did not greatly appeal to Newton in his early days, though Isaac Barrow's edition of the *Elements*, and the influence of Barrow himself, resulted later in a truer appreciation of the value and importance of geometrical method. There were also certain books— the *Optics* of Kepler (1571–1630), Oughtred's *Clavis*, Descartes' *Geometry*, and the works of Wallis (1616–1703)—which Newton studied at Trinity College, all of which helped to prepare the ground for his early discoveries.

The main original contributions of Newton to natural philosophy are dealt with at some length in the three chapters which follow the present survey of his early discoveries. It is, however, no exaggeration to claim that in each of the three main areas of Newton's achievements—pure mathematics, optics, theory of gravitation—the preliminary ground was covered within a very few years of his leaving school. So far as the calculus and the idea of universal gravitation are concerned, the essential work may have been done before Newton was twenty-four, and in optics, before he was twenty-eight years old.

The *Clavis* of Oughtred, a Fellow of King's College, Cambridge, was a textbook on elementary arithmetic and algebra and a work of great merit. It systematised the use of algebraic symbols and introduced much new notation, its author being the leading mathematical teacher during the early part of the seventeenth century. By the middle of the century Oughtred's disciple John Wallis of Emmanuel College, occupied a similar position among mathematicians, having been appointed Savilian professor of geometry at Oxford in 1649. The works of Wallis provided an invaluable groundwork, and by their study Newton would be brought into touch with contemporary knowledge of all aspects of pure mathematics.

From Isaac Barrow, however, Newton gained that enthusiasm for optics and geometry which comes from personal contact. Nor is it likely that Barrow's influence would be limited to academic matters. His career is an interesting example of what could happen to an enterprising and gifted individual amid the uneven tenor of seventeenth century life either in England or on the Continent.

John Evelyn (1620–1706), the diarist, described Barrow as that " excellent, pious, and most learned man, divine, mathematician, poet, traveller, and most humble person ". Charles II was expressing popular opinion when, in 1672, he appointed him Master of Trinity as "the best scholar in Europe". Another side of this versatile individual is seen in the following Court dialogue between the Earl of Rochester, leader of the lighter side of life in the Court at Whitehall, and Barrow, as royal chaplain:

Rochester: Doctor, I am yours to the shoe-tie.
Barrow: My lord, I am yours to the ground.
Rochester: Doctor, I am yours to the centre of the earth.
Barrow: My lord, I am yours to the Antipodes.
Rochester (scorning to be foiled by a musty old piece of
    divinity): Doctor, I am yours to the lowest pit of Hell.
Barrow (turning on his heel): There, my lord, I leave you.

During his comparatively short life, Isaac Barrow saw changes in almost every facet of English life. The old feudal system finally passed away; no longer could the monarch hold the sway of an Elizabethan age; the claim that the Church of England embraced the whole nation had, perforce, been abandoned and the reaction against Puritanism had undermined the reality of religion and public spirit. In Barrow's lifetime also, the change

took place which marked the progress from the scientific world
of Galileo (1564–1642) to that of Newton. The forceful and
energetic personality of Barrow touched most of these issues,
and so far as Newton was concerned, though only twelve years
separated their ages, the influence of Barrow helped to make
possible the full development of the younger man's genius.

Despite Barrow's royalist leaning—his father was Charles I's
linen-draper—and the consequent feeling against him by the
Puritan element, he was elected on his merits as a Fellow of
Trinity. Even the Master of the College, a Parliamentarian, had
been heard to say of him: "Thou art a good lad: 'Tis pity
thou art a Cavalier." Barrow's interest in mathematics is said to
have come through the study of Church history which he found,
through its chronology, depended on astronomy, and thus on
geometry. The difficulties he encountered in teaching himself
Euclid led to the publication in Latin in 1655 of a simplified
edition of the *Elements* for the use of beginners; an English
version followed in 1660. Barrow's royalist sympathies prevented his appointment as Regius Professor of Greek and he
decided to travel for three years—with an allowance of sixteen
pounds a year from his College, and ready money from the sale
of his books.

Barrow's return to England in August 1659 preceded, by only
a few months, the Restoration when Charles II ascended the
Throne. In January 1660, General Monck began his famous
march from Scotland to London, much to the satisfaction of
Barrow, who compiled a Latin poem of some length in his
honour. At Cambridge Charles II was proclaimed King when
at one o'clock on 10 May, 1660, the heads of Colleges were
summoned to the Schools, and brought with them "their Fellows and Scholars in their formalities, with music before them,
and from thence proceeded to the Cross on Market Hill",
where the Proclamation to the University took place.

Then the music brought them back to the Schools again and
there left them, and went up to the top of King's College
Chapel where they played a great while. After the Music had
done, King's bells and all the bells in Town rang till 'twas

night, and then many bonfires were kindled and many garlands hung up in many places of the streets.

Barrow's disappointment at not being appointed Regius Professor of Greek during the Protectorate, was counterbalanced by his election to the chair without opposition after the Restoration. His interest in mathematics resulted also in his appointment in 1662 to the chair of geometry at Gresham College, London. This necessitated a weekly visit to the capital. The ride of about fifty miles each way was made somewhat less arduous by the recent introduction of the public coach, in place of the two-day journey by horse.

The career of Barrow has been outlined at some length, partly in view of his influence on Newton, but also because he is so closely associated with the Restoration atmosphere at Cambridge, into which the young Trinity freshman came from Grantham in 1661. Three years later, Newton was examined in Euclid by Barrow, for a Trinity Scholarship. The interest of Barrow in stimulating Newton's geometrical interests has already been mentioned, though the story that he formed an indifferent opinion of the examinee's knowledge of Euclid does not easily fit in with other facts. Trenchard More, whose authoritative and detailed biography of Newton was published at the University of Cincinnati in 1934, justly refers to Barrow as the intellectual father of Newton.

During his undergraduate years, Newton made one of his earliest discoveries—the binomial theorem—now well known to all who have crossed the threshold of more advanced mathematics. The familiar expansion of $(1 + x)^2$ in terms of powers of x, namely $1 + 2x + x^2$, can be extended to higher powers of $(1 + x)$ by the simple process of multiplication. The binomial theorem gives a formula, or rule, as Newton called it, for writing down the expansion of *any* power of $(1 + x)$. If n represents the power of $(1 + x)$ then:

$$(1 + x)^n = 1 + nx + \frac{n(n-1)}{1 \cdot 2}x^2 + \frac{n(n-1)(n-2)}{1 \cdot 2 \cdot 3}x^3 + \ldots \quad nx^{n-1} + x^n$$

The validity of this rule may easily be checked by giving n various values, each of which is a positive whole number. Newton revealed his genius, however, by applying the rule to cases where n is not a positive whole number. When n is negative or a fraction, the series of terms on the right-hand side has no last term, and is known as an infinite series.

Newton admits the stimulation he received from " the Works of our celebrated countryman Dr. Wallis", but the generalisation known as the binomial theorem far exceeds anything that had been attempted before. The result of Newton's work was communicated in a letter dated 13 June, 1676, to Oldenburg, Secretary of the Royal Society; it was for the information of Leibniz (1646–1716). This letter is an important one and contains a vague hint that Newton had discovered a further method of extending infinite series, but it does not disclose his " method of fluxions "; in the next chapter this method will be discussed in some detail. From the point of view of Newton's early discoveries, it is sufficient here to state that the foundations of his work on fluxions were laid when he was about twenty-three years of age.

The name of Kepler is rightly associated with the three laws of planetary motion, which played such an important part in the subsequent work of Newton on universal gravitation. It may not be so generally well known that Kepler—astronomer, mathematician and mystic—also made important contributions to the study of light; and the word " optics " used in this connection may be taken from the title of one of his works. This was the *Dioptrice* published in 1610, and was the textbook which Newton studied as part of the normal course at Cambridge. It is one of the most important of Kepler's works, containing as it does an account of his invention of the astronomical telescope, which consisted of two convex lenses in place of the one concave and one convex of the Galilean telescope.

Kepler's approach to the study of light, and in particular his work on the astronomical telescope, must have appealed to Newton, who, although attracted by mathematics, had a very practical mind. Among the first of his discoveries at Cambridge was one relating to the passage of light through a glass prism. The prism for this purpose was purchased by Newton at Stourbridge or Sturbridge Fair. This was held about one mile east of Cambridge, near the Priory of Barnwell and to the south of the River Cam. The name has been preserved in a nearby modern street, Stourbridge Grove. Stourbridge Chapel, or Hospital for Lepers, was founded probably in the twelfth century. The Fair was reputed to be the largest in Europe and was held annually from 24 August to 28 September. King John (who reigned from 1199 to 1216) is said to have given the Fair to the Leper Hospital. The annual opening was an event of great pomp and ceremony, and the description by Defoe (c. 1659–1731) of shops in rows like streets, shows the magnitude of the Fair at the time of Newton.

By 1665 Newton had performed experiments with the prism which led to his discovery of the nature of white light, as revealed in the spectrum. His optical studies were interrupted by the Great Plague; this struck Cambridge as well as other parts of England and Newton was forced to retire to his home at Woolsthorpe for two years.

It is, however, by his work on gravitation that Newton will always shine in the popular imagination.

> Sir Isaac Newton was the boy
> That climbed the apple tree, sir;
> He then fell down and broke his crown
> And lost his gravity, sir.

This extract from *The Irish Schoolmaster* expresses, in typically Irish form, the legend of Newton and the apple. The story that a falling apple first directed Newton's thoughts towards gravitation is supported by John Conduitt (1688–1737), his close friend and successor at the Mint, and also by Voltaire (1694–1778) who claims to have obtained it directly from Mrs. Conduitt, formerly Catherine Barton, Newton's favourite niece who lived with him for many years. Conduitt gives the date as 1665 while Voltaire places it in 1666. Either year would include the period of Newton's enforced absence from Cambridge.

It has been justly pointed out that there are no other examples of achievement in the history of science to compare with that of Newton during the two golden years of 1665–67. To his early discoveries in pure mathematics and optics must be added that of the law of universal gravitation. It was a fitting tribute to Newton's genius therefore that he should be appointed in 1669 to succeed Barrow in the chair of mathematics at Cambridge founded by Henry Lucas. Lucas, who was at St. John's College, became secretary to Lord Holland, Chancellor of the University: he also represented Cambridge in Parliament and, according to Barrow, stoutly defended her privileges, "seeing to it that the toga should not become tributary to the soldier's cloke". In his oration on the founding of the Lucasian Chair, Barrow, the first professor continues,

On reaching what might prove the last turning of his mortal course he [Henry Lucas] took counsel with his friends how he could best promote your studies. And when he had decided in what respect you were especially weak—he fixed on Mathematical learning as most deserving of his benefaction.

To modern Cambridge this may come as somewhat of a shock, unless it is remembered that the Elizabethan Statutes had discouraged mathematical studies as not worthy of scholars!

In justification of his own decision to exchange the Greek chair for the mathematical one, Barrow says,

I can see no harm in changing what had become a troublesome burden for a lighter one, by betaking myself from the grammatical-mill to this mathematical wrestling school. For, to be frank, although I never actually disliked Philology, I have always felt a greater affection for Philosophy; and without despising the entertaining pursuit of word-catching, my truest affections have been given to the more weighty search of natural causes and effects.

It has been said that Barrow originated the tradition, persisting until the end of the nineteenth century, that the most finished product of Cambridge was a first-rate mathematician who had devoted considerable attention to the classical languages!

The holder of the Lucasian professorship was expected to lecture publicly, to make himself accessible to inquiring students, and to present a copy of his lectures annually to the Vice-Chancellor of the University. There is no doubt of the mutual work and confidence between Barrow and Newton. In the preface to his optical lectures published in 1669, Barrow acknowledges his indebtedness to Newton for having revised the manuscript, making corrections and suggestions. In the same year Barrow resolved to devote himself to theology and resigned the Lucasian professorship in favour of Newton, who held it until 1702. By that time he had been appointed as Master of the Mint, in London.

It is not surprising that Newton's first lectures were given on optics, in view of his early discoveries on the subject; in fact the years 1668–78 have been called the " optical decade " of his life. The results of his researches were communicated to his students through these lectures, though the latter were not published until 1704. The Lucasian chair also gave Newton an opportunity to develop his researches in pure mathematics and mechanics; the years 1678–87 have been described as the " gravitational decade ". His work during these two decades covered three fields—the calculus, optics and gravitation—and his achievements in any one of them would have assured Newton of a place among the immortals, lifting him beyond the limits of University, nationality and race, making men of science everywhere his debtors. Such a tribute to his memory was paid by the presence of delegates from all over the world at the Tercentenary Celebrations of his birth, organised by the Royal Society and held at Cambridge in 1946. In his address of welcome at Trinity College the Master of the College, Dr. G. M. Trevelyan, made special reference to Newton's early work in Cambridge, and to the sympathetic treatment he received at Trinity. One paragraph of the address in particular is worthy of special note.

In 1661 Newton, at the age of eighteen, came up to Trinity as a Sub-sizar or poor scholar. His Tutor and teacher in mathematics and geometry was Isaac Barrow, not yet Master of the

College, but in 1663 Lucasian Professor of Mathematics in the University. Barrow soon perceived that his pupil was a genius unlike anyone else, and with a noble generosity actually resigned the Professorship of Mathematics in order that Newton should hold it at the earliest possible moment. So at the age of twenty-six Newton became Professor, the acknowledged head of mathematics in all Cambridge, while remaining a Fellow of Trinity College and working in his rooms on the other side of this Court, and habitually dining in this Hall. He had therefore ample leisure and encouragement to proceed with his abstruse calculations, which resulted nearly twenty years later in his publication of the *Principia* in 1687.

One may perhaps wonder what effect Cambridge had on Newton, particularly on his personality and attitude towards other people. The words of the Master of Trinity College, just quoted, point to one or two of the influences which would undoubtedly affect Newton's outlook. The fact that the atmosphere of the college allowed such freedom of development was indeed a prerequisite for the unfolding of genius. The kindly influence of Isaac Barrow provided that sympathetic guidance which enhances the value of freedom. From a nearby college, Emmanuel, Henry More (1614–1687)—one of the Cambridge Platonists—who was a native of Grantham, undoubtedly influenced Newton's views and strengthened his belief in religious toleration; More ultimately became one of Newton's friends. Charles Montagu (1661–1715), later Chancellor of the Exchequer, was a contemporary of Newton at Trinity College, and the influence he exerted on Newton's knowledge of, and interest in, the world of affairs will be discussed later. Companions such as those just mentioned would form a fitting introduction for Newton into the world of people.

With regard to changes that may have taken place in his personality, only speculation is possible where there is no evidence. In Newton's day psychological observers to take note of impulse or inhibition did not exist, and we can only assume that the general atmosphere of the University, the *alma mater*, which has persisted to the present time, would make her own unique contribution towards the development of every undergraduate. Such influences, as those of the buildings and quadrangles in which the university is set, defy expression. There is a story of a College servant rolling the great expanse of grass which adjoins King's Chapel, and a visitor from overseas watching him. The stranger was admiring the smooth surface and cared-for appearance of the lawn and longed to introduce something similar into his own university. Handing a suitable reward he asked for the secret. " You roll this grass backwards and forwards like this, and go on doing it for hundreds of years," was the reply. In this simple incident lies a parable. The accumulated devotion of generations of scholars seems enshrined in the surroundings amid which they lived and thought. Their heritage comes to life as, each year, freshmen take the place of their elders and receive the traditions and attributes of true learning: integrity, accuracy, humility. The integrity Newton revealed in his attitude to hypotheses, the accuracy of detail in his experiments, the humility with which he reviewed his own attainments—all form an integral part of his personality. And there can be little doubt that Newton would be the first to acknowledge his indebtedness both to his contemporaries and to his surroundings at Cambridge.

The uses of the differential and integral calculus are frequently introduced at an early stage into the teaching of mathematics. In particular, young engineering students are trained in the use of the calculus, for it is a powerful mathematical tool useful in the solution of a variety of problems. Nevertheless, this branch of mathematics is still regarded as the preserve of the specialist, and frequently students of other subjects have little or no knowledge of it. It has already been mentioned that Newton made an important contribution to the calculus by devising "the method of fluxions". In order to appreciate the value of his work, some knowledge of this branch of mathematics is, of course, essential: the following general account is therefore written for the benefit of the non-specialist reader.

At the outset it is desirable to direct attention to the word "fluxion", which means "flowing" or "changing": this presupposes that change is taking place, and "fluxions" are concerned with the rate at which the change occurs. This idea of rate of change is made clearer by contrast with the simple ideas of elementary mathematics. Thus, arithmetic deals with the importance of numbers, and the way in which they can be built up, used and combined, so that everyday problems of calculation may be solved. In elementary algebra, letters represent numbers, and problems can be solved which are difficult or even insoluble by the ordinary processes of arithmetic. Some of the practical aspects of geometry, such as simple mensuration, provide further examples of the use of numbers in elementary mathematics: lengths, areas and volumes all have numbers which indicate their magnitude. The symbols and processes of elementary trigonometry, together with the use of appropriate mathematical tables, enable the student to solve more difficult problems involving the dimensions of triangles and other figures.

The simple processes of arithmetic, algebra, mensuration and trigonometry are chiefly concerned with numbers, or with quantities which remain the same throughout the whole or part of a problem. Even when such a problem is concerned with distances traversed, and the time taken in so doing, the distances are expressed as a definite number of units of length, and the times as a definite number of units of time. Similarly, speeds are regarded as constant throughout a given length of time or distance.

Yet even in the simple problems of time and distance a little reflection will show that speeds do not always remain the same during the whole or part of a problem. For example, when planning a motor run of say one hundred miles, an average speed of thirty miles an hour may be assumed, and the time of the journey calculated as three hours and twenty minutes. But the average speed does not represent what actually takes place. The car starts from rest, not with a velocity of thirty miles an hour: its speed varies at different times and depends on many factors such as gradient and condition of the road: the engine can be accelerated to produce increase in speed. Sometimes speed is gained or lost more quickly than at others. The processes of elementary mathematics are not capable of taking into account these irregular changes.

It was in the fourteenth century that a group of Paris philosophers—chief of whom was Nicholas Oresme (1323-82)—seriously tackled this question of motion that was not regular. They described it as "difform" motion, as opposed to "uniform" or steady motion. It was also realised that difform motion itself could increase or decrease in a uniform manner, and to describe this they used the term "uniform difform". This would describe the motion of a car that increased its speed steadily—the modern term being "uniform acceleration". But to most of the men of the fourteenth and later centuries, "uniform difform" would appear as unintelligible as the use of the expression "regular irregular" might seem to us. The strangeness of uniform difform motion was seized on by the contemporaries of Erasmus (1466 or 1467–1536), who ridiculed the Paris school. This brief reference to medieval thought emphasises the fact that although everyone is familiar with the idea of motion, it is not easy to adjust the processes of elementary mathematics to cover the idea of changing motion, or in more exact language, the idea of the "rate of change" of a quantity.

The importance of motion so impressed the Greek philosopher Heraclitus (*c.* 500 B.C.) that he maintained that all things were in a state of flux. It is of interest, though probably only a co-incidence, that the term "fluxion" which Newton employed is directly related to Heraclitus' idea of flowing: in fact, the word is derived from the Latin *fluxio*, which means a flowing or flood.

The rate of change of a quantity indicates how the quantity is increasing or decreasing at a given time. For example, the speed of a car may increase and then diminish, thereby passing through a maximum value: similarly, the speed may decrease and then increase, thereby passing through a minimum value. Nicholas of Oresme had noticed that the rate of increase or decrease of a quantity is slowest in the neighbourhood of a maximum or minimum. No further reference to this fact was forthcoming until the beginning of the seventeenth century, when Kepler stated it again. It was not, however, until Fermat (1601–65) put the result in mathematical form that it became fraught with great possibilities. Although Fermat really used the method of the differential calculus, he only applied it to special examples.

Wherein then is the unique contribution of Newton? It is in the recognition of the generality of the mathematical way of expressing a rate of change. Fermat used it in isolated problems: in Newton's hands it became a powerful mathematical method applicable to all cases which involve a rate of change. Newton used the word "fluxion" to describe this rate of change, and some fifty years after the discovery of the method he referred to his work thus:

I invented the methods of series and fluxions in the year 1665, improved them in the year 1666, and I still have in my custody several mathematical papers written in the years 1664, 1665, 1666, some of which happen to be dated: and in one of them dated 13 November, 1665, the Direct Method of Fluxions is set down.

In this early mathematical paper Newton explains the pro-

Trinity College, Cambridge

Newton's rooms were on the first floor between the Gateway and the Chapel

1 Corporis A in circulo AD versus. D gyrantis, conatus a centro tantus est quantus in tempore AD (quod pono minutissimum esse) deferret a circumferentia ad distantiam DB: siquidem eam distantiam in eo tempore acquireret si modò conatu non impedito libere moveretur in tangente AB.

Jam cùm hic conatus corpora, sic modò in directum ad modum gravitatis continuo urgeret, impelleret per spatia quæ forent ut quadrata temporum: ut noscatur per quantum spatium in tempore unius revolutionis impelleret, quæro lineam quæ sit ad BD ut est quadratum periferiæ ADEA ad AD⁹. Scilicet est BE. BA:: BA. BD (per 3 elem). Vel cum inter BE ac DE ut et inter BA ac DA differentia supponitur infinitè parva, substituo pro se invicem et emergit DE. DA:: DA. BB. faciendo denîq DAY (siu DE×DB). ADEA⁹ ÷ DB. $\frac{ADEA⁹}{DE}$, obtineo lineam quæsitam (nempe quadratum Periferiæ / Diametrum tertiam proportionalem in ratione periferiæ ad diametrum) per quam conatus recedendi a centro in directum constanter applicatus propelleret corpus in tempore unius revolutionis.

Verbi gratia cum ista tertia proportionalis æqeat 19,7392 semidiametros si conatus recedendi ad centro virtute gravitatis tantus esset quantus est conatus in æquatore recedendi a centro propter motum lunæ diurnum: in die periodico propelleret graves per 19¾ semidiametros terrestres siue per 69087, milliaria, et in hora per 120 mill. et in minuto primo per 1/30 mill siue per 100 passus, id est, 500 pedes. Et in minuto secundo per 5/108 ped, siue per 5/9 digit. et tanta est vis gravitatis ut gravia deorsum pellat 160 pedes circiter in 1" hoc est 1350 vicibus longius in eodem tempore quàm conatus a centro circiter, adeóq vis gravitatis est toties major, ut ac terra convertendo faciat corpora recedere et in aëra prosilire.

2 Coroll. Hinc in diversis circulis conatus a centro sunt ut diametri applica quadrata temporum revolutionis, siue ut diametri ductæ in numerum revolutionum factarum in eodem quovis tempore. Sic cum Luna revolvit in 27 dies 7 horis + 43' siue in 27,3216 diebus (cujus quadratum est 746½) ac distat 59 vel 60 semidiametris terrestribus a terrâ. Duco distantiam D 60 in revolutionis lunaris 1; ac distantiam superficiei terrestris a centro quadratum revolutionum 746½, et sic habeo proportionem 60 ad

cess which we now call differentiation. His work was not published until 1674 under the title *Method of Fluxions and Infinite Sequences*. In present-day mathematical language, Newton's "fluxion" is the differential coefficient of the variable quantity which he calls the "fluent".

There is another aspect of the calculus, namely, the integral calculus, in the development of which Newton again showed his genius. In this also, much progress had been made by previous workers. One of the problems which had long puzzled mathematicians was that of finding the area bounded by a curve. It had not been realised that the key to the problem was the connection between it and differentiation. Galileo and his disciple Torricelli (1608–47) had come near to the solution in connection with the falling of heavy bodies and their velocities at any instant. Isaac Barrow extended this to any velocity conforming to given conditions, but even he did not link the problem with the method of differentiation. It has been claimed that where such men failed Newton succeeded because he had recognised the notion of "fluxion" and had formally stated it. In the *Tractatus de Quadratura Curvarum* written in 1671, revised in 1673 but not published until 1704, may be found Newton's considered thought on this aspect of mathematics, namely, the process of finding areas bounded by curves.

One aspect of Newton's work on the calculus deserves more than a passing reference, namely, the controversy with Leibniz. In the history of science there have often been rival claimants for priority of discovery or achievement, but probably the most famous of all such disputes is that between Newton and Leibniz, and their respective supporters, concerning the calculus. The bitterness of the quarrel and the significance for mathematics of the points at issue justify this view. In estimating the place of the controversy in the life of Newton, or of Leibniz, it is essential to collect facts before any imputation of motive can be made, or blame assessed. Though it is clearly beyond the scope of this book to deal exhaustively with the facts, or to reach a final conclusion regarding the contestants, an attempt will be made to indicate what was at issue, and its relation to the atmosphere of the seventeenth century.

When Newton published the *Principia* in 1687, he complimented Leibniz on having invented a calculus similar to his own, except for notation and language; but he did not describe either his own or Leibniz's method. In 1693 Wallis published, in the second volume of his *Collected Works*, a brief account of Newton's fluxions, and in the preface mentioned the calculus as being another name for fluxions. Thus mathematicians had an opportunity of comparing, for the first time, Newton's method of fluxions and Leibniz's calculus. Towards the end of the seventeenth century, mathematicians were therefore becoming skilled in the use of this powerful new tool and were more concerned with its possibilities than with its origin: they called it Leibniz's calculus. Presumably the use of the calculus, both in Britain and on the Continent, would have developed without incident had not a Swiss, Fatio de Duillier, living in England, published a mathematical tract in 1699 which raised the question of priority in discovering the methods of the calculus. We are not concerned with the complicated motives which may have led Fatio, a friend of Leibniz, and afterwards of Newton, to defend the cause of the latter at the expense of the former; suffice it to say that Fatio had developed a personal animus against Leibniz, and an almost fanatical friendship with Newton. The tract contains the following passage:

Compelled by the evidence of facts I hold Newton to have been the first inventor of the calculus, and the earliest by several years. And whether Leibniz, its second inventor, has borrowed anything from him, I would prefer to my own judgment that of those who have seen the letters of Newton and copies of his other manuscripts. Nor will the silence of the more modest Newton, or the active exertions of Leibniz in everywhere ascribing the invention of this calculus to himself, impose upon any person who shall examine these documents as I have done.

Apart from the egoism displayed in Fatio's attack, and the

nature of his language, it is reasonable to ask whether the subject-matter is typical of contemporary feeling towards scientific inquiry. In this connection it will be of interest to survey the prevailing attitude towards plagiarism during the seventeenth century; by so doing it will be easier to appreciate the reactions of Newton and Leibniz to the charges implied in Fatio's statement, and to understand the repercussions both in Britain and on the Continent.

It is recorded that in 1646 Torricelli wrote to his friend Cavalieri (1598–1647), a disciple of Galileo, expressing the fear that knowledge of one of his discoveries should reach the French, who might claim it as their own and publish it first. Later in the same year he announced his discovery, but in 1647 took the precaution of depositing his work with Michelangelo Ricci (1619–1682), an Italian geometer who was later made a Cardinal. Torricelli seems to have had cause for his anxiety, as on a previous occasion, having communicated his expression for the centre of gravity of a cycloid, he had been asked for a proof: this he gave and for two years there was silence —then those to whom he sent the proof claimed priority for its discovery! Torricelli's caution in depositing his work with Ricci did not however prevent Fermat in 1657 writing a letter in which he claimed the discovery as his own, and that he had been in correspondence with Torricelli concerning it. Descartes deliberately left obscurities in his own *Geometrie* in order to avoid being involved in disputes about priority.

A further example of the general atmosphere concerning scientific discovery is the quarrel between Robert Hooke (1635–1703) and Newton. In 1686 the Royal Society decided to publish Newton's *Principia*, eulogising his work on gravitation. In particular Sir J. Hoskyns, President of the Royal Society during 1682–83, and Secretary during 1685–87, said it was more to be prized as it was invented and perfected at the same time. This gave offence to Hooke, especially as he had previously explained his own investigation to Hoskyns. After the meeting of the Royal Society, some of the members visited a coffee-house where

Hooke attempted to prove that he had given Newton the first hint concerning gravitation.

The coffee-house was becoming an important factor in the intellectual life of the times in Britain; but it could easily be responsible for the spread of exaggerated reports. In a letter from Halley (1656–1742) to Newton, dated May 22, 1686, informing him of the recent decision of the Society to publish the *Principia*, Halley adds the following:

There is one thing more that I ought to inform you of, *viz.* that Mr. Hooke has some pretensions upon the invention of the rule of the decrease of gravity being reciprocally as the squares of the distances from the centre. He says you had the notion from him, though he owns the demonstration of the curves generated thereby to be wholly your own. How much of this is so, you know best, as likewise what you have to do in this matter; only Mr. Hooke seems to expect you should make some mention of him in the preface, which 'tis possible you may see reason to prefix. I must beg your pardon, that 'tis I that send you this ungrateful account; but I thought it my duty to let you know it, that so you might act accordingly, being in myself fully satisfied, that nothing but the greatest candour imaginable is to be expected from a person, who has of all men the least need to borrow reputation.

Leibniz also had accused a rival mathematician—Tschirnhausen (1651–1708)—of publishing as his own, much that Leibniz had communicated to him. A modern defender of Leibniz, who absolves him from the charge of copying from Newton, finds himself compelled to suspect Leibniz of using Barrow's work to a very much greater extent than he was willing to acknowledge and of carefully avoiding anything which might lead to a disclosure.

These examples of plagiarism in the seventeenth century, and the atmosphere of suspicion and subterfuge associated with them, emphasise the desirability of taking into account this general background when an inquiry is made into a particular case. It is no wonder that many mathematicians concealed their results, or communicated them without giving proofs, or even hid their work in jumbles of letters. The field of mathematics was ready for exploration; at any moment some fresh aspect or solution of an old problem might be revealed, and there was always the possibility that two independent workers might stumble across a new truth simultaneously. But, as always, human nature and self-esteem were sufficient to create an atmosphere in which it was easy to believe one could claim priority over a fellow student. There was no clearing-house for making known the results of research until the foundation of the learned societies: the *Accademia del Cimento*, at Florence in 1657; the *Royal Society* in 1660; and the *Académie Royale des Sciences* in Paris in 1666. The founding of these societies did not, however, suddenly break the tradition of the earlier part of the century—namely, communication of scientific results by means of letters; such private correspondence persisted long after, and easily led to personal claims which could never have been made if the communication, in the first instance, had been sent to a learned society.

Fatio's charge against Leibniz, and the bitter controversy in which Newton became involved, should be regarded in the light of the foregoing. Leibniz was naturally indignant, and at first believed that Newton was ignorant of it and would vindicate him. The silence of Newton resulted in the publication by Leibniz, in the Leipzig *Acta eruditorum*, of a dismissal of the charges as emanating from a boorish and jealous young man. The editors of the *Acta* declined a reply from Fatio on the ground that their journal was not the medium for personal disputes. The next and more virulent phase of the controversy occurred five years later when, in 1704, Newton published his *Opticks*, which included two mathematical tracts. One of these contained the method of fluxions, and Newton's reason for publishing it is contained in the following words: " Some years ago I lent out a manuscript containing such theorems; and having since met with some things copied out of it, I have on this occasion made it public." The Leipzig *Acta* published an anonymous review, with an appendix in which the writer claimed that Leibniz was the inventor of the calculus and that

Newton had used his work under the title of fluxions. In 1708 John Keill (1671–1721), then Savilian professor of astronomy at Oxford, hinted in a paper in the *Philosophical Transactions* of the Royal Society that Leibniz obtained the idea of the calculus from some of Newton's manuscripts to which he had had access. Leibniz appealed to the Royal Society, but it was not until 1712 that a committee to investigate the matter was appointed. The committee tried to be fair, but Leibniz could hardly be expected to accept its findings as final, since Halley, a strong supporter of Newton, was a member. The report of the committee was in favour of Newton, and in 1713 the relevant letters and papers were published under the title of *Commercium Epistolicum*. The personal controversy lingered until the death of Leibniz in 1716, but the cleavage between Continental and British mathematicians continued throughout the century.

The full significance of the respective contributions of Newton and Leibniz is a matter for the trained mathematician, but the non-technical reader may well appreciate that in any subject the manner of presentation of a new line of thought can be of very great importance. This is especially so where the discovery is in the nature of a mathematical method destined to solve an increasing number of problems. It was pointed out earlier that where Newton differed from his predecessors was in his recognition of the universal application of what he termed "fluxions". The differential notation of Leibniz, on the other hand, has been of outstanding value in the process of perfecting the calculus as a powerful mathematical tool.

As early as 1665 Newton used a dot, placed over the letter to represent the fluxion, e.g. $\dot{x}$, and this notation persisted, especially in Britain; some English writers in the eighteenth century tried to alter the nomenclature though still retaining the dot. In 1675 Leibniz introduced the symbols dx and dy as the differentials of x and y, and also the derivative form $\dfrac{dx}{dy}$. A history of mathematical notation has been published by Professor F. Cajori, of the University of California, and in it he maintains that: "Perhaps no mathematician has seen more clearly

than Leibniz the importance of good notation in mathematics."
It is a tribute to the latter's foresight that $\dfrac{dy}{dx}$ as the differential
coefficient and $\int$ as the sign of integration have stood the test
of nearly three centuries of mathematical progress.

The controversy between Newton and Leibniz unfortunately
assumed an altogether disproportionate place in the relation
of British and Continental mathematicians. As a result, only
the geometrical and fluxional methods introduced by Newton
were studied and used at Cambridge, and with them the "dot"
system of notation. Thus, in spite of the brilliant group of
scholars inspired by Newton among his own countrymen,
further developments in mathematical analysis took place
almost entirely on the Continent. At the beginning of the nineteenth century, however, the tide turned. A Cambridge mathematician, Robert Woodhouse (1773–1827), published a critical
comparison of the Newtonian and Leibnizian notations and
urged the use of the latter's differential notation involving d,
in place of the "dot" notation of Newton. Woodhouse's arguments so impressed three undergraduates—G. Peacock (1791–
1858), J. F. W. Herschel (1792–1871) and C. Babbage (1792–
1871)—that in 1812 they founded the Analytical Society to
advocate *"the principles of pure d-ism as opposed to the
dot-age of the university"*. The subtle humour of the phrase is
attributed to Babbage. Herschel suggested with youthful enthusiasm that the three should enter into a pact to "do their
best to leave the world wiser than they found it"; the introduction of the differential calculus into the Cambridge curriculum was proposed by the others as the first test of their
sincerity. Opposition came from some of the older men, who
wished to keep exclusively to Newton's method of fluxions.
Although Woodhouse was Lucasian professor of mathematics,
it was really due to the efforts of the triumvirate who founded
the Analytical Society that the change was ultimately effected.
The breach between the mathematical descendants of Newton
and those of Leibniz was thus healed, and Cambridge played an
important part in the development of mathematical analysis,

as she had done in guarding and passing on her Newtonian heritage. It is of interest to note that the " dot " notation is still used for the solution of certain problems.

A fitting tribute to the two men whose names will for ever be associated with the methods and notations of the calculus comes from a distinguished French mathematician, Professor J. Hadamard, who represented his country at the Royal Society Newton Tercentenary Celebrations in 1946:

Leibniz had only become acquainted with Newton's discovery, at any rate directly, some years later. Let us simply notice that Newton's creation was one thing, Leibniz's another and that in his epic discoveries the former was not inspired by the latter.

Throughout this chapter frequent reference has been made to the calculus as a powerful mathematical tool. It is not easy for the non-mathematician to realise the far-reaching results of this branch of mathematics. Enough has been written already to indicate the importance of the idea of "rate of change", and it will be readily appreciated how valuable the methods of the calculus are in the realm of engineering, where complicated changes in motion may occur. Further, the areas of surfaces, and volumes of solids frequently require the methods of the calculus for their evaluation, as do also centres of gravity and moments of inertia. The calculus is indispensable in problems involving the bending of beams under stress, and in assessing strengths of materials. The modern study of aerodynamics and the kindred science of hydrodynamics would be impossible without the principles of the calculus. In the somewhat different realm of statistics the use of the calculus is also fundamental. Another important application of the method is the mathematical treatment of curves. The characteristics of many curves, as well as of the sections of a cone, were known to the Greeks. The study of curves formed a considerable part of the work of Greek geometers. To Apollonius of Perga (fl. B.C. 225) is ascribed a treatise on conic sections, and the name of Archimedes of Syracuse (B.C. 287–212) is perpetuated in the well-known Archimedean spiral. Mathematicians of the seventeenth century also were specially interested in the study of curves; some of the latter are still known by the names of the men who first investigated their properties; for example, the Cartesian ovals, and the lemniscate of Bernoulli. The introduction of analytical geometry by Descartes provided a new approach to all such problems, and Newton devised a method of finding the shape of a curve near the origin of coordinates.

Although the study of curves may seem to be the concern of the pure mathematician, their properties are of considerable importance in engineering design. For example the cycloid, associated with the names of Galileo, Descartes, Wren, Pascal, Huygens, is well known to a wide public in the familiar variable gear of the modern bicycle, housed entirely in the rear hub shell and worked on the epicyclic principle, by which all toothed wheels are constantly in mesh.

One of the most valuable applications of the differential calculus may be found in problems involving maxima and minima. If y is a function of x, the equation $y = f(x)$ may be plotted by using the usual Cartesian coordinates. Now it is known that the value of the differential coefficient at any point on the curve varies with the angle that the tangent at the point makes with the axis of x. In passing through a maximum or minimum, the inclination of the tangent becomes zero, so that points of maxima and minima may be found by equating the differential coefficient to zero. Problems of maxima and minima arise in a variety of subjects, but the following application to natural history is of special historical interest in view of its Newtonian background.

This particular problem has reference to the economy of wax used by the honey-bee in sealing the ends of the hexagonal prisms containing the honey in the honeycomb. In view of the widening scope of natural philosophy in the seventeenth century, it is not surprising that the same individual may reveal such diverse interests as the study of mathematics and observations of the habits of bees. James Philip Maraldi (1665–1729) was born at Perinaldo in the county of Nice, and owed much of his success as an astronomer to the training and influence of his maternal uncle John Dominic Cassini (1625–1712). Maraldi's astronomical work included cataloguing stars in such detail that he could establish that certain faint objects, up to then regarded as stars, were in fact comets. His observations of planets were equally meticulous and in 1700 he was employed under Cassini in prolonging the French meridian to the northern coast of France, and later at Rome he advised on the construction of the meridian through the baths of Diocletian. Maraldi's interest in natural history was by way of relaxation from the arduous task of mapping the heavens. On his return to France in 1703, he presented natural history specimens, chiefly collected at Verona, to the Académie Royale des Sciences, to which body he had been admitted a member in 1699. The *Histoire de L'Académie Royale des Sciences* for the year 1712 contains a memoir by Maraldi, "observations on Bees", and in one section Maraldi gives the measurement of the angles of the three rhombuses of wax by means of which the bees seal the hexagonal prism containing the honey. The acute angles measured 70° 32′ and the obtuse ones 109° 28′. The naturalist Reaumur (1683–1757), whose name is perpetuated in the Reaumur temperature scale, refers to Maraldi's measurements, in volume five of his *Memoires pour servir a l'histoire des insectes*. It occurred to Reaumur that the magnitude of the angles which Maraldi had measured might be those required mathematically for sealing the hexagonal cells so that the least quantity of wax would be used in relation to the volume of honey contained in a cell. Reaumur accordingly asked a German geometer, Koenig (1712–57) to investigate the problem. Koenig's calculations confirmed the conjecture of Reaumur, though his results showed a discrepancy of two minutes of arc from Maraldi's observations. This slight difference remained unexplained until the Scottish mathematician and friend of Newton, Maclaurin (1698–1746), and later the Swiss L'Huillier (1750–1810), not using the same method, found that the difference of two minutes of arc was due to an error in the calculations of Koenig, and not to a mistake on the part of the bees!

The mathematicians whose names have just been mentioned

are but a few of the many whose inspiration will for ever be associated with the name and work of Isaac Newton. By the nineteenth century the mathematical tools had been well tried, and were ready for use throughout the whole realm of studies included in the comprehensive term—modern science.

It was pointed out in the last chapter that some ideas of the calculus had been anticipated prior to Newton's outstanding contribution of the method of fluxions. To appreciate the importance of the latter, it was necessary to estimate the work of other mathematicians. It is equally essential to survey the background of Newton's contribution to optics. But whereas in the case of the calculus, the work of his predecessors and contemporaries can only be fully realised by the trained mathematician, it is somewhat easier to discuss theories and experiments in connection with light, because everyone has first-hand experience of the subject itself.

In the sphere of optics Newton's predecessors were acquainted with certain definite properties of light such as reflection and refraction. The ancient world used mirrors and burning glasses; the geometers of the Platonic school recognised that light travels in straight lines and that when it is reflected at any surface, the angle made with the normal to the surface by the incident beam is equal to that made with the normal by the reflected beam. For the more complicated statement which the law of refraction requires, it is necessary to define more precisely the terms angle of incidence, reflection and refraction. If a normal be drawn to the surface at the point where the incident ray meets it, the angle between the normal and the incident ray is called the "angle of incidence" and that between the normal and the reflected ray the "angle of reflection". In the case of a ray of light being refracted, if the normal is produced into the transparent medium, the angle it makes with the refracted ray is called the "angle of refraction". Ptolemy in the second century drew up tables giving the values for the angles of incidence and the angles of refraction of a beam of light passing from air into glass and water, but it was not until the beginning of the seventeenth century that Willebrod Snellius or Snell (1591–1626), Professor of Mathematics at Leyden, discovered the law of refraction. In its familiar form this law states that when light falls upon the surface of a refracting medium, such as glass or water, the sine of the angle of incidence bears a constant ratio to the sine of the angle of refraction. This trigonometrical statement of Snell's law was arrived at independently by Descartes and by James Gregory (1638–75). Kepler did not reach the law of refraction but realised that the angle of the refracted ray increases less quickly than the angle of incidence when light passes from a rarer into a denser medium. His observations were based on the results of Vitellio (fl. 1254) a Pole, who had compiled a table of the angles of incidence and refraction of light at the surface of water and glass more accurate than the corresponding results given by Ptolemy.

The early part of the seventeenth century produced an exceptional man in the person of Descartes, philosopher and mathematician. The well-known " *cogito ergo sum* "—" I think, therefore I exist "—formed the basis of his approach, and the fact that he is referred to as the father of modern philosophy shows the esteem in which he has been held by later generations. His application of the methods of algebra to the problems of geometry heralded a new era in mathematics. The adjective " Cartesian " is therefore aptly applied both to philosophy and to geometry. Rene Descartes was born in 1596 at La Haye, some thirty or forty miles from Tours, and his life may be divided into three periods. The early years to 1612 included his education at the Jesuit College of La Flèche, which had been founded in 1604 under the active and generous patronage of King Henry IV of France. The second, to 1628, included his voluntary military service under Prince Maurice of Nassau, the son of William the Silent, Prince of Orange. Descartes left his native land in 1617 and served under Prince Maurice in Holland. After four years of varied military experience, he gave up soldiering in 1621 and travelled widely through Europe. The third period, from 1628 to his death in 1650 at Stockholm, may be called the constructive period of his life, and was spent in meditating and writing in great seclusion. During this period he lived chiefly in Holland.

It is not, however, the overlap of a few years in the lives of Newton and Descartes that is of significance in estimating the former's work. It is that Descartes' system of the universe, worked out in accordance with his philosophical ideas, was well known and widely accepted throughout Europe just at the time when Newton at Cambridge was beginning his mathematical and physical discoveries. Descartes maintained that there could be no empty space, but that every part of the universe is filled with particles, so that a particle could only move by taking the place of other particles. So far as the subject of optics is concerned, light was regarded as a pressure, transmitted through the particles, which reached the eye just as the presence of an object is made known to a blind man by the pressure or resistance which travels to his hand through his stick. It is not necessary for our present purpose to pursue further the details of Descartes' system of the universe; some reference to his scheme of vortices will be desirable when dealing with the problem of motion. From the point of view of scientific method, it should be noted that Descartes' theory of light was not based on experiment so much as on the theory that empty space could not exist. Descartes' theory was criticised by Robert Hooke who had been appointed Curator of Experiments of the Royal Society in 1662. Hooke defined light as " a quick vibratile movement of extreme shortness" which should be regarded as propagated instantaneously in all directions: his theory therefore was not greatly in advance of Descartes' instantaneous pressure. It will be seen later that though he agreed with Newton's experimental results, Hooke challenged the theory which Newton built on them.

Newton's aptitude for making things must have stimulated his interest in a very practical aspect of optics, namely, the construction of telescopes. It is not therefore surprising that in his early days at Cambridge his attention was turned to the improvement of the existing type of such instruments. The first telescope was developed by Hans Lippershey (died 1619), an optician of Middelburg, in the Netherlands, whose assistant, according to one account, had noticed accidentally that two spectacle lenses, held in a certain position, had the effect of enlarging the appearance of objects, but showing them upside down. At any rate, there is evidence that in 1608 the claims of Lippershey for either remuneration for his invention, or a privilege, to prevent imitations for thirty years, were discussed by the governing body of the Netherlands. Galileo improved on Lippershey's instruments and used a convex and a concave lens, thereby showing an object to the observer the right way up. Successive telescopes by Galileo improved the magnification to such an extent that it was possible to distinguish not only the surface of the moon, but also four of Jupiter's satellites and, ultimately, the peculiar appearance of Saturn, which in 1656 was first described as a "ring" by Huygens.

Up to the time of Newton, the telescopes in use were refracting ones: that is, they depended on the light from the distant object passing through a lens—the object glass—and forming an image which was ultimately magnified by means of the eyepiece. Now the thicker the lens of the object-glass, the more blurred and coloured is the image, and this distortion is magnified when viewed through the eyepiece. It will thus be appreciated that although a larger object-glass is desirable to take in more light from say, a distant planet, the image becomes increasingly difficult to see in detail. This blurred effect is known as chromatic aberration. Descartes had recognised this difficulty, and believed that if he used a specially shaped object-glass instead of the usual one with surfaces like the surface of a sphere, the chromatic aberration would disappear. The curves discovered by Descartes for this purpose are still known by his name—Cartesian ovals.

Newton's approach was more practical. Before his time it had been assumed that light, the ordinary white light from the sun, was pure; this belief was founded on the idea, handed down from time immemorial, that the sun's light was perfect. Newton's desire to improve the refracting telescope of his day naturally centred round the disadvantages of the blurred and coloured images due to chromatic aberration. The fact that colours were produced when light shone on thick pieces of glass, such as those used in chandeliers, had long been known. Newton set to work to investigate what actually happened when light from the sun fell on a glass prism. It has already been pointed out that the resulting production of the spectrum was

F

one of his earliest discoveries: it proved the foundation of all his work on light and led to his giving up the idea of improving the refracting telescope, and as a result, working on the construction of a reflecting one.

Newton's first scientific paper on light was published in the Royal Society's *Transactions* in 1672, and was concerned with its nature. Referring to this paper Professor L. T. More writes:

In the first place, it is an almost perfect model in both form and content. It is the more remarkable because Newton had no example to follow; it is significant that his first essay was as perfect as was his later work. His mind seemed to need no period of growth but to have reached its full maturity at once.

The opening sentences of Newton's paper have become historic.

To perform my late promise to you, I shall without further ceremony acquaint you, that in the beginning of the year 1666 (at which time I applied myself to the grinding of optic glasses of other figures than spherical,) I produced a triangular glass prism, to try therewith the celebrated phenomena of colours. And for that purpose having darkened my chamber, and made a small hole in my window shuts, to let in a convenient quantity of the sun's light, I placed my prism at his entrance, that it might be thereby refracted to the opposite wall. It was at first a very pleasing diversion to view the vivid and intense colours produced thereby; but after a while applying myself to consider them more circumspectly, I was surprised to see them in an oblong form; which according to the received laws of refraction, I expected would have been circular.

This and similar experiments led Newton to the well-known proposition: "To the same degree of refrangibility ever belongs the same colour, and to the same colour ever belongs the same degree of refrangibility." The modern term for "refrangibility" is "refraction".

The effect of Newton's communication is revealed by the following order made by the Royal Society:

that the author be solemnly thanked, in the name of the Society, for this very ingenious discourse, and be made acquainted that the Society think very fit, if he consents to have it forthwith printed, as well for the greater conveniency of having it well considered by philosophers, as for securing the considerable notices thereof to the author against the arrogations of others. Ordered also, that the discourse be entered in the register-book, and that the Bishop of Salisbury, Mr. Boyle, and Mr. Hook, be desired to peruse and consider it, and bring in a report of it to the Society.

The mention of Hooke's name brings to mind another unfortunate controversy—a forerunner of Newton's later dispute with Leibniz—and provides a further example of the atmosphere of the seventeenth century towards scientific discovery. Robert Hooke (spelt also Hook) was born at Freshwater, Isle of Wight, in 1635. Like Newton he was a weakly child who became keenly interested in mechanical inventions. He was educated at Westminster School under Dr. Busby, and at Christ Church, Oxford. His ability was recognised by a group of natural philosophers at Oxford, outstanding among whom was the Hon. Robert Boyle (1627–91), an Irishman who is said to have been described, after the manner of his country, as "the Father of Chemistry and Uncle of the Earl of Cork". Hooke became a friend and personal assistant of Boyle in the latter's experiments, and it is on record that Boyle, with other prominent members of the Royal Society, formed a company to exploit Hooke's inventions, particularly his application of a coiled spring to timepieces. It was in his capacity as Curator of the Royal Society that Hooke was included among the three appointed to consider Newton's contribution of 1672 on the subject of light. The difference of opinion did not arise from the experiments, but from the interpretation which Newton put on them, Hooke claiming that his own vibratory theory of light was consistent with the facts. Both men appear to have been of jealous nature concerning the originality of their own work, and the unpleasant consequences of the dispute must have contributed to Newton's reluctance thereafter to make known his discoveries to the world. A few months later Newton wrote to Oldenburg, the Secretary of the Royal Society, that he did not intend to be "further solicitous about matters of Philosophy. And therefore I hope you will not take it ill if you find me cease from doing anything more in that kind." Later Newton was at pains to clear himself in respect of Hooke's insinuation that he had used the latter's *Micrography*, published in 1664.

It is indeed fortunate that Newton did not adhere to his intention to cease from further participation in natural philosophy, for he was yet to give to the world his *Opticks*, and above all the *Principia*. The results of Newton's work on light were, unlike the *Principia*, written in English and ultimately published in 1704 as *Opticks: or, a Treatise of the Reflections, Refractions, Inflections and Colours of Light*. It has been suggested that Newton delayed publication until after Hooke's death in 1703 in order to avoid further controversy. There is the story also of the loss by fire in 1692 of a large work on optics, containing Newton's experiments and researches of twenty years, the fire being caused by a dog called Diamond during Newton's absence from his rooms whilst attending Chapel at Trinity College. From whatever cause the delay in publication arose, the *Opticks*, in the words of Professor Sir Edmund Whittaker, "after being esteemed for three generations chiefly as a historical landmark displaying a marvellous combination of theoretical and experimental skill, is now once more being read for its living scientific interest".

The "advertisement", or preface, which Newton wrote to the first edition of the *Opticks* begins:

Part of the ensuing Discourse about Light was written at the Desire of some Gentlemen of the Royal Society, in the Year 1675, and then sent to their Secretary, and read at their Meetings, and the rest was added about twelve Years after to complete the Theory; except the third Book, and the last Proposition of the Second, which were since put together out of scatter'd Papers. To avoid being engaged in Disputes about these Matters, I have hitherto delayed the printing, and should still have delayed it, had not the Importunity of Friends prevailed upon me. If any other Papers writ on this Subject are got out of my Hands they are imperfect, and were perhaps written before I had tried all the Experiments here set down, and fully satisfied my self about the Laws of Refractions and Composition of Colours. I have here publish'd what I think proper to come abroad, wishing that it may not be translated into another Language without my Consent.

This paragraph was written when Newton was over sixty years old and it is therefore yet another interesting comment on his reticence and desire to avoid controversy.

Newton's *Opticks* is divided into three books. The opening sentence of the first is typical of his approach to all scientific investigations: " My Design in this Book is not to explain the Properties of Light by Hypotheses, but to propose and prove them by Reason and Experiments: In order to which I shall premise the following Definitions and Axioms." Then, in Part II of the first book, follow propositions concerning colours. The second book contains four parts. The first contains observations concerning reflexions, refractions and colours of thin transparent bodies, including the phenomenon of " Newton's rings ", and the coloured appearance of soap bubbles. The same part contains remarks on the foregoing observations. Part III includes propositions on the permanent colours of natural bodies, and the analogy between them and the colours of thin transparent plates. The observations of Part IV deal with the reflexions and colours of thick transparent polished plates. The third book opens with observations concerning the inflexions of rays of light, and the colours made thereby, in other words the diffraction of light—a term introduced by the Italian physicist Grimaldi (1618–63) in his treatise on light published in 1665. In fact, Newton prefaces his own observations on the phenomenon thus:

Grimaldo has inform'd us, that if a beam of the Sun's Light be let into a dark Room through a very small hole, the Shadows of things in this Light will be larger than they ought to be if the Rays went on by the Bodies in straight Lines, and that these Shadows have three parallel Fringes, Bands or Ranks of colour'd Light adjacent to them. But if the Hole be enlarged the Fringes grow broad and run into one another, so that they cannot be distinguish'd.

The subject of diffraction played an important part in the development of the wave theory of light at the hands of Thomas Young (1773–1829), a medical graduate of Cambridge and Professor of Natural Philosophy at the Royal Institution, London, and Augustin Fresnel (1788–1827), a civil engineer and head of the department of public works in Paris. It is characteristic of Newton as a man of science that at the close of his observations on diffraction he should write:

When I made the foregoing Observations, I design'd to repeat most of them with more care and exactness, and to make some new ones for determining the manner how the Rays of Light are bent in their passage by Bodies, for making the Fringes of Colours with the dark lines between them. But I was then interrupted, and cannot now think of taking these things into further Consideration. And since I have not finish'd this part of my Design, I shall conclude with proposing only some Queries, in order to a farther search to be made by others.

In the second edition of the *Opticks*, published in 1714, there follow thirty-one queries which reveal Newton's ideas on the properties and nature of light and the way in which the eye receives light rays: there is reference also to the phenomenon of polarisation, which was first described by Erasmus Bartholinus, a Danish philosopher (1625–98) and afterwards more exactly by Huygens (1629–93).

Newton's reference to Huygens is no trivial or casual one; behind it there moves a figure of outstanding eminence in the seventeenth century—one of the greatest scientific geniuses of all time. Christian Huygens was born at Amsterdam; his gifted father Constantine corresponded for many years with Descartes and this friendship was not without influence on the development of Christian. When Newton was only three years of age, the young Huygens, then a boy of about sixteen, was deeply impressed by Descartes' writings. In later life he referred to them thus: "everything in the world became clearer and I was sure that when I found some difficulty that it was my fault that I did not understand his [Descartes'] thought. I was then only fifteen or sixteen years old." This profound influence of Descartes on Huygens may possibly have been a misfortune for the latter, preventing him from reaching those heights of natural philosophy achieved by his younger contemporary, Newton. Huygens did not go as far as Descartes in allowing intuition to take precedence over experiment: neither did he agree with Newton's "hypotheses non fingo" (I do not frame hypotheses). The place of hypothesis in scientific method was, in fact, at the basis of the main difference between the views of the two men.

The classic work that contains Huygens' theory is his *Treatise on Light*, consisting of six chapters, of which one, Chapter V, "On the Strange Refraction of Iceland Crystal", gives an account of the polarisation of light. The wave theory is contained in Chapter I, "On Rays Propagated in Straight Lines". Huygens' Preface to his treatise emphasises the fact that in the seventeenth century, many discoveries were made independently.

I have desired to relate these particulars to make known how long I have meditated the things which I now publish, and not for the purpose of detracting from the merit of those who, without having seen anything that I have written, may be found to have treated of like matters: as has in fact occurred to two eminent Geometricians, Messieurs Newton and Leibniz, with respect to the Problem of the figure of glasses for collecting rays when one of the Surfaces is given.

Huygens' wave theory of light admits an analogy with sound. Referring to the way that light spreads, he writes: "that which can lead us to comprehend it is the knowledge which we have of the spreading of Sound, in the air." He realises that wave motion involves the question of time and so maintains that light has a velocity. In order to account for the phenomenon of the eclipse of the moon by the earth, Huygens recognises that the velocity of light must be very great. It will be remembered that Descartes formulated instantaneous propagation of light by means of pressure through space. Of this Huygens writes:

For it has always seemed to me that even Mr. Des Cartes, whose aim has been to treat all the subjects of Physics intelligibly and who has assuredly succeeded in this better than anyone before him, has said nothing that is not full of difficulties, or even inconceivable, in dealing with Light and its Properties.

Huygens' insistence on the necessity of light having a definite velocity was justified in 1675 by Rœmer (1644-1710), a Danish astronomer who, with Huygens and J. D. Cassini from Italy, adorned the court of Louis XIV. Rœmer's measurement of the velocity of light was based on a comparison of the calculated and observed times of the eclipses of Jupiter's satellites: but the velocity of 186,000 miles a second is, for practical purposes, instantaneous so far as terrestrial distances are concerned.

In any appreciation of Newton's theory of light it must be remembered that his ideas were tentative, as indicated in the extract from Book III of the *Opticks* quoted earlier. In Query 25 Newton maintains that the double refraction associated with a crystal of Iceland spar is an instance of another original property of rays of light. The inability of the supporters of the wave theory at that time to account for the polarisation of light gave added support to Newton's "corpuscular theory". He pointed out that although Huygens, in order to explain double refraction, supposed two vibrating mediums within the crystal, he (Huygens) confessed himself at a loss for explaining them. Newton's Query 29 is of special significance: "Are not the rays of Light very small Bodies emitted from shining Substances?" Newton shows how such a theory accounts for the various properties of light, and in particular the double refraction of Iceland spar. Queries 30 and 31 are complementary: "Are not gross Bodies and Light convertible into one another, and may not Bodies receive much of their Activity from the Particles of Light which enter their Composition?", and "Have not the small Particles of Bodies certain Powers, Virtues or Forces, by which they act at a distance, not only upon the Rays of Light for reflecting, refracting, and inflecting them, but also upon one another for producing a great part of the Phenomena of Nature? " The days of the electromagnetic theory of light were some two centuries distant, but the breadth of Newton's vision is significant. For a hundred years the corpuscular theory held sway, until Fresnel introduced with brilliant success a guess that Hooke made in 1672, namely, that light vibrations are transverse, or *perpendicular* to the direction of propagation, and not longitudinal like those of sound. Huygens' wave theory thus came into its own. A careful study of Newton's theory reveals that it has a considerable periodic or wave element in it; in modern physical theory, it is necessary to give light both wave properties and particle properties; but it must not therefore be thought that Newton could have foreseen this need, though a striking tribute was recently paid by Academician S. I. Vavilov, of the U.S.S.R. at the Newton Tercentenary celebrations of the Royal Society: " It may be said that Newton saw through ' classical physics ' right down into its profoundest depths, and right out into its ultimate scope."

In view of the enormous benefits that have accrued to observational astronomy as a result of Newton's optical discoveries, it may not be inappropriate to make some reference to these before considering his contribution to theoretical astronomy, namely the law of universal gravitation. One of the papers read at the Newton Tercentenary Celebrations organised by the Royal Society in 1946 was by Dr. W. S. Adams, of the Mount Wilson Observatory, entitled "Newton's Contributions to Observational Astronomy". Referring to the study of the origin of colours and the invention of the reflecting telescope, he writes:

Newton's contributions to astronomy were so numerous and so varied, due to the rare combination which he possessed of a powerful analytical mind and great practical ability and skill in observation, that we sometimes forget in thinking of his discovery of gravitation and the laws of motion, and of the co-invention with Leibniz of the differential calculus, that his study of colours forms the basis of the science of spectroscopy, and that his tiny reflecting telescope has developed into the most efficient tool for the study of the universe that man has ever devised.

The very name spectroscopy is a reminder of the term spectrum (Latin "appearance") introduced by Newton.

All previous workers had assumed that white light was distinct from and independent of any light coming from a coloured object. Newton's experiments on the separation of a beam of white light into beams of different colours formed the basis of spectroscopy and his careful observation of the phenomena now known as "Newton's rings" made possible the researches of later physicists in explaining them. The study of spectra, which includes methods of obtaining, observing and photographing spectra and the measurement of wavelengths, has developed, as spectroscopy, into a science which provides an important method of investigating atomic structure and also has various other applications in physics, chemistry and astronomy.

With regard to the other outstanding contribution to observational astronomy mentioned by Dr. Adams, namely the reflecting telescope, it is only right to mention that James Gregory in 1663 had proposed a reflecting telescope consisting of two concave mirrors mounted facing one another. Light from a distant object was to be reflected from the larger of the two mirrors to the smaller one, and brought to a focus where the image could be magnified by means of an eyepiece. Newton improved on this idea by replacing the smaller concave mirror by a small plane mirror set at $45°$ with the axis of the telescope. The rays were thus reflected through a hole in the side of the telescope tube, instead of passing through a hole in the centre of the large concave mirror as suggested by Gregory. It is a tribute to Newton's craftsmanship that he was the first actually to construct a reflecting telescope. This was completed successfully towards the end of 1668: it was only $6\frac{1}{4}$ inches long with an aperture of $1\frac{1}{3}$ inches. Newton claimed that the magnification was equal to that of a refracting telescope six feet in length.

This little instrument easily showed the disk of Jupiter and four satellites and, with difficulty, the phases of Venus.

The Royal Society heard of the existence of a reflecting telescope and requested Newton to send them an instrument for inspection. This he did in 1671 by presenting the Society with a similar telescope of $6\frac{1}{3}$ inches focal length and magnification of 38 diameters: this instrument is now one of the most treasured possessions of the Society. Newton was at once proposed for election, and elected as a Fellow on 11 January, 1672. The honour which had been conferred was much appreciated by the recipient, and, as a result, Newton offered to communicate the result of his experiments with a prism. On 6 February, 1672, he sent to Oldenberg the paper to which reference was made earlier in this chapter.

At this point it may be appropriate to indicate in general terms the nature of Newton's contributions to the study of light. In the first place there is the analysis of sunlight based on his experiments with a prism; the importance of the spectrum with its significance for the modern science of spectroscopy; the phenomena of colours; the permanent colours of natural bodies and the colours of thin transparent bodies—the experiment revealing " Newton's rings ". Secondly, there is the contribution which Newton made to the theory of light based on the notion of corpuscles being emitted from a luminous source, in contrast to the wave theory of Huygens. In the third place, and by no means least in importance, is Newton's contribution to observational astronomy. Not only did he provide the foundation on which the modern science of astronomical spectroscopy is built, but he also had the distinction of constructing the first reflecting telescope.

As the science of spectroscopy has developed, particularly in connection with stellar radiations, so the need for more light for the photographic plate has increased. There are limits to the dimensions of the refracting telescope, as apart from mechanical difficulties of mounting, an increase in the thickness of object-glasses causes loss of light to which the photographic plate is most sensitive. In the case of a reflecting telescope, increase in the size of the mirror carries with it increase in direct light from the distant object.

Thus Newton's tiny instrument, with its metal mirror of 1-inch diameter, has become the prototype of the many large reflecting telescopes throughout the world, the largest having a glass surface of 200 inches diameter. In particular, American astronomers have produced instruments of outstanding power, operating at observatories whose sites have been chosen for their exceptionally good atmospheric conditions. One of the greatest difficulties to be overcome in the construction of these large instruments is that of making the mirror. The 100-inch tele-scope at Mount Wilson Observatory, California, is an example. The only firm that would undertake the casting and annealing of so large a surface was the St. Gobain glassworks in Paris. After preliminary trials a disk was produced 101 inches in diameter, 13 inches thick and more than $4\frac{1}{2}$ tons in weight. As three melts had to be poured into the mould in quick succession, small bubbles of air became trapped and the long anneal-ing process caused loss of strength and rigidity. On its arrival at Pasadena, near Los Angeles, the American astronomers Hale and Ritchey thought that the disk would not be able to retain a good surface figure. The management of St. Gobain expressed their willingness to bear the loss and to construct a better disk. But their efforts were not successful and then the First World War intervened. The failures led Hale to proceed with the original disk and subsequently the telescope was successfully completed, having taken its name from Hooker, a Los Angeles business man, who financed the scheme.

For some time Hale had considered the possibility of an even larger mirror. In fact in 1928 he wrote:

Starlight is falling on every square mile of the Earth's surface and the best we can do is to gather up and concentrate the rays that strike an area 100 inches in diameter. I have never liked to predict the possibilities of large telescopes, but the present circumstances are so different from those of the past that less caution seems necessary. The question remains whether we could not safely advance to an aperture of 200 inches or, better still, to twenty-five feet.

This question was answered on 3 June, 1948, at the dedication ceremony on Palomar Mountain of the largest of all reflecting telescopes; and as a fitting tribute, a bronze plaque was unveiled bearing the following inscription: "The 200-inch telescope is named in honour of George Ellery Hale whose vision and leadership made it a reality." The mirror for this was made at the Corning Glass Works, New York.

In Newton's own country a lasting memorial to his reflecting telescope may be found in the 98-inch instrument at the Royal Greenwich Observatory, Herstmonceux, Sussex—fittingly named the Isaac Newton Telescope. This, too, has a unique history. In 1946 the Royal Astronomical Society responded to the appeal of its President, Professor H. H. Plaskett, for greater emphasis on observational astronomy, and the Council of the Society supported his idea of building a large reflector. Earlier, in 1930, a similar instrument of 85 inches had been planned for the observatory of the University of Michigan, designed by H. D. Curtis, the director. The first disk proved unsuitable, but the Corning Glass Company offered a 98-inch one, and this subsequently was cast and annealed. Owing, however, to lack of funds, and the death of Curtis in 1942, the scheme was abandoned. Eventually, through the generosity of the University of Michigan and the Tracy McGregor Fund, the disk was presented to the Royal Greenwich Observatory for the Isaac Newton telescope at Herstmonceux. This happy reminder of the co-operation and friendship of the English-speaking peoples, is also a tribute to Newton, who in the realm of science may justly be acclaimed a citizen of the world.

Many of Newton's discoveries in the calculus, optics and gravitation were made soon after his undergraduate days. In fact, in later life he looked back to the years 1665 and 1666 as the period when he was at the height of his powers in natural philosophy. These years were spent at Woolsthorpe owing to the prevalence of the plague at Cambridge. The following extract is taken from a memorandum written when Newton was about seventy-three years old; it is preserved in the Portsmouth Collection of his papers, and shows the development of his ideas on motion and gravitation. Referring to the year 1666 he writes:

I began to think of gravity extending to the orb of the moon, and having found out how to estimate the force with which a globe revolving within a sphere presses the surface of the sphere, from Kepler's rule of the periodical times of the planets being in a sesquialterate proportion of [to the power 3/2] their distances from the centres of their orbs [see page 99], I deduced that the forces which keep the planets in their orbs must be reciprocally as the squares of their distances from the centres about which they revolve: and thereby compared the force requisite to keep the moon in her orb with the force of gravity at the surface of the earth, and found them answer pretty nearly. All this was in the two plague years of 1665 and 1666, for in those days I was in the prime of my age for invention, and minded mathematics and philosophy more than at any time since.

Newton's debt to his predecessor is acknowledged in this extract and there can be little doubt that Kepler should be reckoned among the "giants" to whom reference is made in the well-known phrase of standing on their shoulders. The importance of Kepler's work is more easily seen if his place among contemporaries is recognised. Sir David Brewster (1781–1868), who held the post of vice-chancellor of Edinburgh University, published a volume entitled *The Martyrs of Science. Lives of Galileo, Tycho Brahe, and Kepler*. Brewster's valuable memoirs of Newton have already been quoted, and his own achievements in physics give him the right to speak on the

importance of such pioneers. In the opening paragraph of the
life of Kepler he writes:

It is a remarkable circumstance in the history of science, that
astronomy should have been cultivated at the same time by
three such distinguished men as Tycho, Kepler, and Galileo.
While Tycho, in the 54th year of his age, was observing the
heavens at Prague, Kepler, only 30 years old, was applying his
wild genius to the determination of the orbit of Mars, and
Galileo, at the age of 36, was about to direct the telescope to
the unexplored regions of space.

The diversity of gifts which Providence assigned to these three
philosophers was no less remarkable. Tycho was destined to lay
the foundation of modern astronomy, by a vast series of accurate
observations made with the largest and the finest instruments.
It was the proud lot of Kepler to deduce the laws of the planetary orbits from the observations of his predecessors; while
Galileo enjoyed the more dazzling honour of discovering by the
telescope new celestial bodies, and new systems of worlds.

In different ways, all suffered persecution or hostility at some
point in their careers, and so could be regarded as martyrs of
science. But also the word martyr, in its original meaning of
witness, is peculiarly applicable to these pioneers, who through
their witness testified to different aspects of astronomy and
mathematics, and prepared the way for the generalisations of
Newton.

At the early age of sixteen, Tycho Brahe grasped the fact that
only through a steadily pursued course of observation would it
be possible to obtain a better insight into the motions of the
planets, with the object of deciding which system of the world
could be regarded as the true one. Other European astronomers
seem to have failed to appreciate the necessity of such observations; they were content to regard the Ptolemaic system
as fundamental and to ridicule the ideas of Copernicus.
Ptolemy's astronomical treatise, well known through its Arabic
title the *Almagest*, dates from the second century A.D. and is a
complete exposition of the views and theories of Hipparchus
(*c.* 190–120 B.C.) who was not only the greatest of Greek astro-

nomers, but also one of the greatest of all time: to him is due the invention of trigonometry and a catalogue of the positions of over a thousand stars. The *Almagest* preserved the great science of astronomy built up by the Greek observers and geometers, together with additional material by Ptolemy himself. For some fourteen centuries, until the time of Copernicus (1473–1543), this book received scientific authority, and the geocentric system of the universe was accepted without question. It is said that Hipparchus was nearly persuaded to adopt the heliocentric views of his contemporary Seleucus the Babylonian. It is an interesting speculation how far the course of history and thought, and indeed of Newton's work, might have been different had the author of the *Almagest* taken the sun, instead of the earth, as the centre of the universe.

Tycho Brahe ultimately produced observational evidence in support of the Copernican theory; his work was done chiefly at Uraniborg (meaning "The City of the Heavens") a castle constructed in 1576 for astronomical observations on the island of Hveen, about fourteen miles from Copenhagen. Ultimately Brahe settled in Prague, Czechoslovakia, and here in 1600 he attracted Kepler.

If Tycho Brahe saw the importance of observations accurately made and carefully recorded, it fell to Johann Kepler to make important deductions in accord with all the observed facts. As in the case of Brahe, Kepler's early life did not seem calculated to prepare him for the discovery of the laws of planetary motion which have made his name immortal. In 1596 his researches were published in a work *Prodromus of Cosmographical Dissertations; containing the cosmographical mystery respecting the admirable proportion of the celestial orbits, and the genuine and real causes of the number, magnitude, and periods of the planets, demonstrated by the five regular geometrical solids.*

At the turn of the sixteenth century Kepler heard from Brahe that he had been able to determine the eccentricity of the planets more accurately than hitherto, and so began the series of negotiations that ended with Kepler's appointment as assistant to Tycho. On the latter's death in 1601, Kepler succeeded him as

Imperial mathematician. He had been entrusted with the task of examining the orbit of Mars, and in 1609 he published his great work *The New Astronomy, or Commentaries on the Motion of Mars*; the discoveries recorded therein form the basis of physical astronomy. Kepler found that the uniform circular motion and the cycles and epicycles, with which Copernicus had endeavoured to explain the planetary inequalities, did not agree with the observed facts. He was thus led to the first two of the laws which bear his name: (1) The planets travel in paths which are ellipses with the sun at one focus; (2) The areas swept out in any orbit by the straight line joining the centres of the sun and a planet are proportional to the times. A third law, (3), that the squares of the periodic times which the different planets take to describe their orbits are proportional to the cubes of their mean distances from the sun, was not made known by Kepler until 1619 when it appeared in a remarkable volume entitled *The Harmonies of the World*, which was dedicated to James I of England. As its name suggests, this work contained much which is of an astrological nature.

Both Tycho Brahe and Kepler may justly be regarded as medieval: at times the language employed by the latter is so fanciful that the reader may be more impressed with Kepler's astrological and mystical sympathies than with his insight into the fundamental laws of planetary motion. Between Kepler's background and that of Newton lies a great gulf, but there is one man who genuinely bridges this gulf. In fact an eminent historian of science, Sir William Cecil Dampier, writes: "In a very real sense Galileo is the first of the moderns; as we read his writings, we instinctively feel at home; we know that we have reached the method of physical science which still is in use today." Galileo combined the observational skill of Tycho Brahe with the theoretical insight of Kepler. Through his telescope, fresh vistas were revealed in moon, planets and stars, and by means of his mathematical gifts the science of motion was created. A wider outlook than that of his predecessors may justly be attributed to Galileo, and in a unique manner he prepared the way for Newton.

Galileo's acquaintance with a telescope dates at least from 1609. On a visit to Venice he learned from common rumour that a Dutchman, Hans or John Lippershey, had presented to Prince Maurice of Nassau an optical instrument which possessed the singular property of causing distant objects to appear nearer the observer. The Galilean telescope, known at first as Galileo's tube, as has been said, shows a direct image whereas that made by Lippershey, the spectacle-maker of Middelburg, probably produced an inverted image and so was the prototype of the astronomical telescope. Galileo's discoveries were contained in his *Nuncius Sidereus* (the Sidereal Messenger) published in 1610 and dedicated to Cosimo de Medici, Grand Duke of Tuscany. The four satellites of Jupiter were named by Galileo Medician Stars in honour of his patron. Later discoveries included the crescent of Venus, the Rings of Saturn and the spots on the Sun. The reception accorded to Galileo's discoveries was varied: Kepler, so far from disbelieving the existence of the four Medician stars, longed for a telescope to support his own theory (based on Euclid's five regular solids), and contained in his *Cosmographic Mystery*. According to the theory he maintained that there should be two planets round Mars, six or eight round Saturn, and perhaps one each round Mercury and Venus. This is an example of the mystical interpretation of the universe so characteristic of Kepler.

On the other hand, the supporters of the Aristotelean views were vehement in their opposition. Arguments were used which would now be inconceivable. One of the Florentine astronomers maintained that as there were only seven apertures in the head —two eyes, two ears, two nostrils, and one mouth—and as there were only seven metals, and seven days in the week, so there could be only seven planets. Again, as the moons of Jupiter are invisible to the naked eye, they can exercise no influence on the earth; and being useless, they do not therefore exist. Another writer declared that he would never concede his four new planets to that Italian from Pisa, even if he should die for it.

The most substantial part of Galileo's work consisted in his contributions towards the establishment of mechanics as a science. Some valuable but isolated facts and theorems had been previously discovered and proved, but it was Galileo who first clearly grasped the idea of force as a mechanical agent. The interdependence of motion and force was not indeed formulated into definite laws by Galileo, but his writings on dynamics are everywhere suggestive of those laws, and his solutions of dynamical problems involve their recognition. In this branch of science he paved the way for Newton. The city of Pisa provided the setting for some of Galileo's experiments. A new idea began to dawn in his mind, namely, that it is not steady motion but change of motion that implies force. The mass moving under no force would enjoy constant velocity in constant direction, but when a force acts upon it, then its velocity or its direction or both will vary.

The revolutionary character of Galileo's work lay in his belief that motion could be maintained without the presence of a force. The Aristotelean idea that all moving bodies require the application of force to keep them in motion had for centuries been regarded as fundamental, both with regard to movement on the earth and on the grander scale of the heavenly bodies. The ancient story of Phoebus' car—the chariot and horses by whose means the sun is daily driven across the sky— illustrates this desire to demand a visible application of force to explain motion.

It was the generalisation of Newton that transformed Galileo's ideas into a system of dynamics embracing all movement, whether terrestrial or celestial. The essence of the problem was recognised by him from the day when he pondered over the fall of an apple. Newton's originality, however, did not consist in the belief that a force was responsible for the flight of an apple to the ground, but that the nature of the force was the same as that which caused the moon to move round the earth, or the planets to maintain their several orbits round the sun. This conception was not merely a suggestion; as already pointed out, Newton was averse to ideas or " hypotheses " as he called them —theories unsupported by facts. Aristotle had propounded theories, some of which had been refuted by the experiments

101

of Galileo. For Newton, generalisations from the latter's observations of the motion of bodies on the earth had to be substan-
tiated also at the bar of experiment. Fortunately, sufficient
material concerning the motion of the heavenly bodies had
already been collected. Their positions, obtained from the laws
which Newton believed applied to all cases of motion, could
thus be checked with the results of actual observation. In the
Principia Newton gives a clear statement of the laws of motion,
deduced from the dynamical experiments of Galileo. The first
two may be briefly summarised thus: (i) absence of force
implies uniform motion in a straight line; while (ii) rate of
change of motion is determined by force. The third law (iii) is
the well-known statement that action and reaction between
two bodies are equal and opposite.

Although Newton's thoughts turned to "gravity extending
to the orb of the moon" as early as 1666, his ideas on universal
gravitation were not made known to the world until the publication of the *Philosophiae Naturalis Principia Mathematica,*
in 1687. The experimental evidence in favour of the theory, and
the difficulties which delayed publication, are in themselves
revealing, and form a suitable study of this aspect of Newton's
discoveries.

Newton was not alone in his desire to connect the force that
impels an object to fall directly towards the centre of the earth
with the forces that control the motions of the moon and
planets. Within a few years of the granting of the Royal Charter
to the Royal Society in 1662 this problem had become prominent, and discussions of it took place also in the houses of members specially interested. Among these were Sir Christopher
Wren, Seth Ward, who was Bishop of Salisbury, Sir Robert
Boyle, Robert Hooke and Edmond Halley. In January 1684,
Halley met Wren and Hooke, and the latter claimed that he
had demonstrated all the laws of celestial motion. Halley
admitted his own lack of knowledge of the subject and in a
letter to Newton he describes Wren's offer of a book worth forty
shillings to the man who within two months could bring a
convincing demonstration of Hooke's claim. Apparently Wren

doubted Hooke's assertion that his reason for not making public the result of his work was that others, trying and failing, might value it the more when it was ultimately published.

When Halley visited Cambridge in August of the same year, he asked Newton what would be the path of a body moving under the action of a central force which varied as the inverse square of the distance from the centre. Newton's attitude was typical of his lack of interest in work he had completed, and his lack of desire to see it in print. He said that he had solved this problem and promised to look for his former proof. As this could not be found, Newton worked at the problem, sending his solution to Halley in November 1684. As a result, Halley again visited Cambridge to persuade Newton to place his work before the Royal Society; in December Halley reported to the latter and referred to a treatise of Newton *De Motu* (concerning motion) which he had seen at Cambridge. The full title *Propositiones de motu*, was registered at the Royal Society in February 1685. The events which led to the actual publication of Newton's results are referred to later.

The generalisations of Newton depended on the laws of Kepler. The third law, as already noted, stated that the squares of the periodic times which the different planets take to describe their orbits are proportional to the cubes of their mean distances from the sun. Both Huygens and Hooke saw that this implied a force towards the sun, which, acting on the several planets, varied inversely as the square of their distances from the sun. There were, however, two points which had to be realised before the complete law of gravitation could be enunciated. The first was to show that the law of the inverse square not only explained Kepler's third law, but also the other two—namely (i) elliptical orbits with the sun in one focus and (ii) equal areas described in equal times. The second outstanding point was to show that the gravitation of the earth, on the basis of the inverse square law in relation to the sun, extended to the moon also.

The methods by which Newton solved these two problems are contained in the *Principia*, and it is the reasoning which he employs that gives to this book its unique standing, and justifies the adjective "universal" as applied to gravitation. The generalisations which he made lead to the law of universal gravitation, namely, that two bodies mutually attract one another in direct proportion to the product of their masses and in inverse proportion to the square of their distance apart.

The law, as just stated, may appear simple, but a little reflection will soon reveal a complication concerning what is meant by the distance apart of two bodies. For example, in the case of the earth and the moon, from what point on or within the earth's surface is the distance to be measured? And likewise, to what point on or within the moon? If the masses of the two bodies may respectively be regarded as concentrated at two points, the distance would then be found by measuring the distance between the two points. But what justification is there for assuming, in the case of the earth, regarded as a sphere, and the moon likewise, that the distance apart demanded by the law of gravitation is the distance between the centres of the two spheres? Newton's calculations had been based on the assumption that the sun and the planets could all be treated as though they were concentrated at their respective centres, through which the various attractive forces were presumed to act. Is this correct, or is it merely an approximation due to the enormous distances apart of the various bodies? It was probably the recognition of this problem by Newton that delayed the publication of his results for some twenty years; rather than the fact that his original calculations suffered through being based on an incorrect estimate of the earth's radius.

Newton worked out this aspect of the problem of gravitation on the assumption that each particle of the sun attracted an external particle with a force directly proportional to the product of the masses of the two particles and inversely proportional to the square of their distance apart. It emerged that if the sun were of uniform density, or consisted of a system of concentric shells, each of uniform density, then the resultant force on the external particle is the same as that which would be exerted by the whole mass of sun concentrated at its centre. Newton's meticulous care in avoiding unnecessary hypotheses is well illustrated in what has just been written. His use of the word "hypothesis", and its philosophical implications, are discussed in a later chapter.

Some two hundred years later, when Newton's work could be seen in its true perspective, a fitting reference to the importance of the demonstration mentioned in the last paragraph was made by Dr. J. W. L. Glaisher in an *Address on the bi-centenary of the publication of Newton's* Principia, *1887:*

No sooner had Newton proved this superb theorem—and we know from his own words that he had no expectation of so beautiful a result till it emerged from his mathematical investigation—than all the mechanism of the universe at once lay spread before him. . . . It was now in his power to apply mathematical analysis with absolute precision to the actual problems of astronomy.

The emphasis that has rightly been placed on the word "universal" with reference to the law of gravitation, reveals the true significance of Newton's discovery. "Gravity", so frequently limited in men's minds to the earth, extends to the orbits of satellites round their planets, to the orbits of the planets round the sun, to the periodic paths of comets, and indeed to the whole realm of the heavenly bodies.

In the long story of literary achievement, some authors have
been so closely associated with a particular work that the name
of the one immediately suggests the other. For example, Homer's
Iliad, Euclid's *Elements*, Darwin's *Origin of Species*. At the
beginning of the second half of the seventeenth century
appeared Milton's *Paradise Lost*, using the medieval conception of the heavens; towards its close Newton's *Principia* presented a vista of the Universe that heralded the approach of
modern science. This abbreviated and homely title, the *Principia* or *Principles*, is taken from the more formal *Philosophiae
Naturalis Principia Mathematica*—the mathematical principles
of natural philosophy.

Reference was made at the end of the previous chapter to
the bi-centenary of the publication of the *Principia*. In 1927, on
the occasion of the two hundredth anniversary of Newton's
death, S. Brodetsky, Professor of Applied Mathematics in the
University of Leeds, directed special attention to the uniqueness of the *Principia*. " Its theorems and methods, principles
and laws, are pronouncements that humanity has studied for
generations. Some of the greatest triumphs of human thought
have been achieved as the direct consequence of Newton's
genius." From the system of mechanics contained in the *Principia*, Laplace, Lagrange and their successors were able to set
out the positions and motions of members of the solar system
with such accuracy that astronomical prediction seemed almost
infallible.

There are many examples: the preparation of the *Astronomical Ephemeris* years in advance, and the accuracy of its contents; the well-known return of Halley's Comet at the time anticipated; the prophecies concerning planets then unknown, but
identified later. The classic example of the last is the discovery
of the planet Neptune, associated with the names of J. C.
Adams, and the French astronomer Le Verrier. Irregularities
which never exceeded the tiny angle of two minutes of arc,
were observed in the motion of Uranus, the planet discovered
by Sir William Herschel in 1781. Adams came to the conclusion
that these perturbations were due to the presence of a hitherto

unobserved planet, the position of which he determined, using, of course, Newtonian mechanics. Le Verrier was also working independently on the same problem. In 1846 observations were made at Berlin and Cambridge confirming the existence of the planet as predicted by both Adams and Le Verrier.

Newton's reluctance to make known his discoveries must arouse curiosity as to how the *Principia* came into being. Fortunately information on this is not wanting. In the course of the preparation of Sir David Brewster's larger edition of his life of Newton, there appeared in 1838 a tract written by S. P. Rigaud, Savilian Professor of Astronomy at Oxford, entitled *Historical Essay on the First Publication of Sir Isaac Newton's Principia*. The original material contained in this tract came chiefly from a number of Newton's own MSS. in the collection of the Earl of Macclesfield, and from papers belonging to the Royal Society. Rigaud's essay is an able statement and comprehensive summary of the origin of the *Principia*. Published in 1687, the latter represented Newton's mature judgment and, having been written in the comparatively short space of eighteen months, it possesses a unity made possible by the author's concentration on the theme as a whole. Newton's first approach to the problem of gravity was made at his home in Woolsthorpe as early as 1666. Another landmark in the development of his ideas is the year 1679 when he resumed, after an interval, his early work on the subject. As the application of the inverse square law to the motion of the moon did not agree with its observed motion, Newton had abandoned further investigation.

However in 1679, correspondence, which may certainly be described as friendly, passed between Hooke and Newton. The latter's reply to Hooke shows that by November of that year Newton had again interested himself in dynamics. He maintained that the path of a heavy body, allowed to fall under gravity from a considerable height, would reach the earth eastward of the perpendicular, contrary to popular belief that " if the earth moved, heavy bodies in falling would be outrun by its parts and fall on the west side of the perpendicular ". Newton then continues his reply to Hooke by suggesting the following experiment. The extract is given in full as it reveals Newton's meticulous attention to detail:

The advance of the body from the perpendicular eastward will in a descent of but 20 or 30 yards be very small, and yet I am apt to think it may be enough to determine the matter of fact. Suppose then in a very calm day a pistol bullet were let down by a silk line from the top of a high building or well, the line going through a small hole made in a plate of brass or tinn fastened to the top of the building or well, and that the bullet when let down almost to the bottom were setled in water so as to cease from swinging, and then let down further on an edge of steel lying north and south to try if the bullet in setling thereon will almost stand in a equilibrio but yet with some small propensity (the smaller the better) declined to the west side of the steel as often as it is so let down thereon. The steel being so placed underneath, suppose the bullet be then drawn up to the top and let fall by cutting clipping or burning the line of silk, and if it fall constantly on the east side of the steel it will argue the diurnal motion of the earth. But what the event will be I know not, having never attempted to try it. If anybody would think this worth their trial, the best way in my opinion would be to try it in a high church or wide steeple, the windows being first well stopped; for in a narrow well the bullet possibly may be apt to receive a ply from the straightened air near the sides of the well, if in its fall it come nearer to one side than to another. It would be convenient also that the water into which the bullet falls be a yard or two deep or more, partly that the bullet may fall more gently on the steel, partly that the motion which it has from west to east at its entering into the water may by means of the longer time of descent through the water, carry it on further eastward and so make the experiment more manifest.

At this time Newton also reopened the question of the moon's motion. His early work on gravitation had been handicapped by his use of an incorrect result for the earth's radius. It was now possible for him to base the numerical part of the gravitational theory on a recently revised estimate of the earth's radius made by the French mathematician and astronomer Jean Picard

(1620–82). It is a matter of some interest that in 1666 when Newton was working on gravitation at Woolsthorpe, Picard was appointed astronomer in the Académie Royale des Sciences at Paris. Louis XIV entrusted him with the task of measuring a degree of the French meridian. This work was carried out during 1670–71 near Paris, with an error of only a few yards. The results of Picard's investigation are recorded in Volume VII of the *Memoires de l'Académie Royale des Sciences*. The original unit used was the "Toise de Paris" (about a fathom). The results were also recorded in the units of certain other countries. Thus the degree of a great circle is given as 57,060 toises and as 737/200 "Milles d'Angleterre de 5,000 pieds chacun". The communication of such results to learned societies like the Academy in France and the Royal Society in England obviated the need for carefully worded letters from one scientist to another in making known original work. The new procedure also tended to lessen the plagiarism and suspicion so characteristic, in some quarters, of the seventeenth century.

The next stage in the story of the origin of the *Principia* is associated with the visit of Halley to Cambridge in 1684. Mention has already been made in the last chapter of the prize of forty shillings offered by Wren to the man who could bring a convincing demonstration of Hooke's claim concerning the laws of celestial motion. Fortunately Newton did not limit himself to this aspect of gravitational theory, but after Halley's visit to Cambridge in August 1684, he had so advanced his investigations that by the autumn he had prepared nine lectures which were given in the Michaelmas Term 1684 under the title "De Motu Corporum" (of the Motion of Bodies). The manuscript of these lectures may be considered as a rough draft of the beginning of the first book of the *Principia*.

The two years prior to the appearance of the *Principia* in 1687 may be regarded as the period of preparation for the actual work itself. This period however was by no means tranquil. Looking back it is remarkable that the treatise was not withdrawn from publication. This threat arose partly through the serious shortage of funds suffered by the Royal Society, and partly through the controversy between Hooke and Newton.

The final preparation of Newton's tract *Propositiones de Motu* which Halley was instrumental in introducing to the Royal Society, and which was registered there in February 1685, took longer than had been anticipated. As its contents were ultimately included in the *Principia*, the importance of the tract may easily be overlooked. When it is recognised as the foundation of the system of the universe, its worth cannot be over-estimated. On 21 April, 1686, Halley communicated a paper on Gravity to the Royal Society, and after referring to the truths established by Galileo, Torricelli, Huygens and others he mentions those "now lately discovered by our worthy countryman, Mr. Isaac Newton, who has an incomparable Treatise of Motion almost ready for the press". On the following Thursday, 28 April, Halley's optimism was justified by a further reference in the *Philosophical Transactions of the Royal Society*. "Dr. Vincent presented the Society with a manuscript treatise, entitled *Philosophiae Naturalis Principia Mathematica*, and dedicated to the Royal Society by Mr. Isaac Newton." The MS. referred to was only the first book of the *Principia*, but such was the confidence of the Society in it, that a letter of thanks was sent to the author and a resolution passed at the same time that the printing should be referred to the Council. In June 1686, the Council of the Royal Society ordered that "Mr. Newton's book be printed", but they added "that E. Halley shall undertake the business of looking after it, and printing it at his own charge, which he engaged to do". The latter statement may cause surprise, as its Charter gave the Royal Society power to appoint its own printer and engraver: in fact, the works of various authors were frequently patronised and adopted. It was this very generosity which made financial help towards the publication of the *Principia* impossible, for earlier in 1686 several hundred pounds had been spent on Willughby's four volumes on the *History of Fishes*. Even so, many of the numerous plates had been contributed privately, Pepys being responsible for about eighty of them. The situation was indeed fraught with irony for Willughby's work was so little in demand that one hundred and twenty-five complete sets of *De Historia Piscium* were still unsold by 1740.

The action of Halley in meeting the expenses of publication of the *Principia* is seen to be all the more praiseworthy when his own financial position is realised. Not only was he faced with the upbringing of a young family, but in addition his father had just died and the patrimony on which the son had previously relied had almost completely dwindled away. Posterity's debt to Halley is best understood by imagining the retardation of scientific progress had the *Principia* remained in manuscript form.

But Halley was faced with another problem of quite a different kind. Human frailty is proverbial and even men of genius such as Robert Hooke and Isaac Newton were subject to its baleful influence. The incident involving Halley has already been described in Chapter IV, in connection with the subject of plagiarism in the seventeenth century (see page 67). The correspondence arising from Hooke's claims grew to considerable proportions, and in much of this may be discerned a clash of personalities. Hooke has been described as "the universal claimant". Rouse Ball points out his wide interests in nearly every scientific question then discussed, and that "had he concentrated his efforts, his great ability would doubtless have led him to many valuable discoveries; but usually his conclusions were hasty and incomplete, while his assertions as to what he had proved were sometimes reckless, and are unconfirmed by his extant papers".

The twentieth century is more concerned with an appreciation of a scientist's work, especially in relation to the background in which he lives, rather than a detailed assessment of blame in controversy over priority, which in the seventeenth century played a disproportionate part in scientific progress. The present tendency is to recognise the limitations and weaknesses of a Newton without detracting from the greatness and originality of his contributions to science. For those who still feel the lure of weighing the evidence for and against their hero, perhaps the best advice is that of Rouse Ball. At the end

H

of his essay on the *Principia* he collects numerous letters and memoranda involving Newton, Halley and Hooke, together with Hooke's statement of his case " so that the reader can judge for himself of the justice of the assertion ".

From such unfortunate episodes it is a pleasure to turn to the contents and methods of Newton's *magnum opus*. The title page of the first edition of *Philosophiae Naturalis Principia Mathematica* describes the author as of Trinity College, Cambridge, Lucasian Professor of Mathematics and Fellow of the Royal Society. Under the word *imprimatur* appears the name of Pepys as President of the Royal Society, and then the date 5 July, 1686. The page concludes with the year of publication MDCLXXXVII.

The whole was written in Latin, the common medium of communication of the learned world of those days; this is a reminder also of the versatility of the European student in acquiring fluency of expression in a language other than his own. The ode to Newton by Edmond Halley, which follows the title page, has been translated by Leon J. Richardson, Professor of Latin in the University of California. The dedication is as follows:

To the Illustrious Man

Isaac Newton

and this his work

done in fields of the mathematics and physics a signal

distinction of our time and race

The ode is too long to quote in full, but the first two and the last stanzas give some indication of its nature:

Lo, for your gaze, the pattern of the skies!
What balance of the mass, what reckonings
Divine! Here ponder too the Laws which God,
Framing the universe, set not aside
But made the fixed foundations of his work.

The inmost places of the heavens, now gained,
Break into view, nor longer hidden is
The force that turns the farthest orb, The sun

Exalted on his throne bids all things tend
Towards him by inclination and descent,
Nor suffers that the courses of the stars
Be straight, as through the boundless void they move,
But with himself as centre speeds them on
In motionless ellipses. Now we know
The sharply veering ways of comets, once
A source of dread, nor longer do we quail
Beneath appearances of bearded stars.

Then ye who now on heavenly nectar fare
Come celebrate with me in song the name
Of Newton, to the Muses dear; for he
Unlocked the hidden treasuries of Truth:
So richly through his mind had Phoebus cast
The radiance of his own divinity.
Nearer the gods no mortal may approach.

The *Principia* consists of three Books. The first two are concerned with the problem of motion under the title "De Motu Corporum", and the third, "De Mundi Systemate", deals with the problems of the solar system. Thus Book I refers to the motion of bodies in unresisting mediums; Book II to the motion of bodies in resisting mediums; Book III contains the application of the results of the first two books to the explanation of the solar system. The law of universal gravitation, so justly associated with the name of Isaac Newton, together with deductions from it concerning the relative masses of the sun and planets, occupy but a tenth of the whole work. The remainder of the *Principia* deals chiefly with the mathematical treatment of motion—a subject which, as already pointed out, heralded the beginning of the scientific revolution.

Newton's approach to the principles of dynamics, given in Book I of the *Principia*, has formed the basis of textbooks on the subject to the present time. The description includes the three well-known laws of motion (see page 102 above) and corollaries from them such as the parallelogram of forces, and the theorems relating to systems of particles. Galileo's treatment of the problems of motion was of the utmost importance, but it was due to Newton that the laws of motion assumed a form of universal application, and it was he who clearly distinguished between mass and weight: mass being an indication of the quantity of matter, whereas its weight is the force by which the mass is attracted towards the centre of the earth.

About half the *Principia* gives Newton's views on dynamical problems which have nothing to do with the theory of gravitation. Indeed two sections are of special interest because of original work in the pure geometry of conics, the curves formed by the intersection of a plane with a cone.

Even when the principles of motion have been adequately stated, their application may raise difficulties. This is notably so when the resisting nature of the medium in which motion takes place is considered. Newton devotes Book II of the *Principia* to such problems and includes a comparison of theory with observation of a pendulum whose oscillations are resisted by the air. Another comparison is that between the theory of wave-motion and the phenomena of light and sound. There are also propositions concerning the theory that light is due to corpuscles emitted by a luminous source. In Book III certain astronomical problems receive special attention within the framework of gravitational theory. These may be better understood by considering some of the aspects of Kepler's laws. Although these laws are in accord with observations based on a comparatively small number of revolutions of the planets round the sun, it was known that there were small deviations from exact ellipses. These are called "perturbations" and would, through the centuries, have an appreciable cumulative effect. In fact as long ago as Eudoxus (*c.* 400 B.C.) something was known of these changes in the case of the moon's orbit round the earth, but no satisfactory explanation was possible until the idea of universal gravitation was recognised. Newton's theory at once implies that the moon is not only attracted by the earth, but also by the sun and planets. The dominant influence is of course the earth, about which the moon revolves: other attractive forces, notably that of the sun due to its great mass, cause the perturbations. It does not require a great deal of knowledge of mathematics to realise the difficulty of solving problems which involve the paths of three or more bodies moving under their mutual attractions. Not only did Newton show that the attractive force of the sun would explain the general features of the known perturbations of the moon, but he also predicted others that were not observed until later.

Another important subject included in the *Principia* is an explanation of the tides: this is based on the attraction of the sun and moon on the waters of the ocean. When the attraction of the sun is in the same direction as that of the moon, the total force on the water is at its greatest. The effect on the water is therefore also greatest, and is seen in the phenomena of " spring" tides. These occur at intervals of approximately twenty-nine days at new moon when the moon is between the earth and the sun. On the other hand, when the moon is remote from the sun with reference to the earth, namely at full moon, the forces of attraction due to these two masses oppose one another, and the resultant pull on the water has its least value, with the consequent low tides, known as " neap" tides. By comparing the greatest and least heights of the tides, Newton was able to calculate the mass of the moon.

The earth is not an exact sphere but an oblate spheroid; the attractions of the moon and sun on the slight protuberance at the equator causes a small change in the direction of the earth's axis. The resulting slow conical motion of the earth's axis is called "precession" and has a period of about 26,000 years. It may be added that "nutation" is a slight oscillatory motion of the earth's axis which disturbs the otherwise uniform conical precessional motion. Towards the close of Book III Newton shows how to find the precession of the equinoxes.

In the section on comets with which the *Principia* ends, Newton proved that these bodies move in elliptic or parabolic orbits under the attractive force of the sun. From a practical point of view he applied these theoretical considerations to trace the appearances of a comet which was seen before Julius Caesar's assassination in 44 B.C. Shakespeare makes Calpurnia, Caesar's wife, urge her husband not to leave home on the Ides of March:

> When beggars die there are no comets seen;
> The heavens themselves blaze forth the death of princes.

With regard to the mathematical tools employed by Newton, it is convenient to discuss those available to him from other sources and those of his own invention. Of the former, the following may be described as well-established contributions to mathematics: Euclid on straight lines and Apollonius on conic sections, together with elementary algebra similar to that taught in schools today. More recent, however, was the application of algebra to the problems of geometry, developed by Descartes and known as analytical geometry. Of the tools of Newton's own invention, reference has already been made to his work on algebraic series such as the binomial theorem, and to his discovery of the calculus. Professor T. A. Cherry, of the University of Melbourne, Australia, in a lecture " Newton's *Principia* in 1687 and 1937 ", given to commemorate the two hundred and fiftieth anniversary of the publication of the *Principia*, referred to the mathematical resources at Newton's disposal: these tools had to be utilised in problems of an entirely novel type; so that, in a very real sense, we may say that the whole of the mathematics of the *Principia* was Newton's original creation. Cherry points out that in reading the book it is often possible to discern beneath the surface the sequence of ideas we should nowadays employ, but whereas we should dress the ideas in the notation of algebra and the calculus, and handle them accordingly, Newton dressed and handled them, as far as possible, as pure geometry. It seems probable that he did this, partly because he had a personal preference for geometrical methods, and partly because he was anxious to present his demonstrations, as far as he could, with the standard mathematical language and methods familiar to his contemporaries, so that any question of the validity of his results might not be confused with that of the validity of new methods.

The Royal Society's reception of Newton's memoir *De Motu* in 1684, with the interest it had aroused in the scientific world generally, had prepared the way for the *Principia*—itself first published in 1687. The author's fame spread at home and abroad and inevitably the remainder of his career bore the impress of his rise to world stature. The secluded life of a student could no longer be maintained; his reputation demanded publicity, and from the publication of the *Principia*, Newton himself emerged a public figure. The fortunes, and misfortunes of his new life form the subject of the next chapter; but for the present the history of the *Principia* must be traced from its first appearance in 1687.

The first edition was a small quarto containing 500 pages, illustrated with diagrams in the form of woodcuts, bound in calf, and sold at nine shillings per copy. In a letter dated July 5th, 1687, Halley writes:

I have at length brought your book to an end, and hope it will please you. The last errata came just in time to be inserted. I will present from you the book you desire to the Royal Society, Mr. Boyle, Mr. Paget, Mr. Flamsteed, and if there be any else in town that you design to gratify that way: and I have sent you to bestow on your friends in the University 20 copies, which I entreat you to accept. . . . I hope you will not repent you of the pains you have taken in so laudable a piece, so much to your own and the nation's credit, but rather, after you shall have a little diverted yourself with other studies, that you will resume those contemplations wherein you had so great success, and attempt the perfection of lunar theory, which will be of prodigious use in navigation, as well as of profound and public speculation.

The reference to lunar theory had a sequel. When pressed by Halley to complete this, Newton replied that " it made his head ache and kept him awake so often that he would think of it no more ". No doubt this confession has found a sympathetic echo in the experience of many lesser mathematicians!

Eminent students of natural philosophy bought and studied the *Principia*. It is said that a Scotsman copied it out by hand in order to obtain a copy! The work also aroused the interest of men of letters. Various stories are associated with these non-mathematicians. One, nearing the end of his life, hoped that

Newton would permit him to point out some difficulties. The reply was gracious: "I do not wonder that in reading a hard book you meet with some scruples, and hope that those you propound may help you to understand it more easily." Then Newton answers the questions very fully, and says that he trusts that his correspondent will write again if there be anything else at which he "sticks much". One nobleman, a literary man, asked Newton if there was any method of mastering the subject other than by the study of mathematics. When told there was not, he engaged a tutor for the sum of fifty guineas; but alas, the task was too great and the Earl abandoned it in despair.

The limits of the present book do not permit detailed reference to the considerable correspondence in which Newton took part concerning the *Principia*. Two scholars in particular, Locke and Bentley, reflected the general desire of Newton's contemporaries to understand the significance of his discoveries even though they were not equal to the mathematical discipline involved. Locke consulted Huygens as to the technical accuracy of Newton's work and then confined himself to an appreciation of its general nature. Bentley consulted Newton before publishing certain lectures which he had delivered in refutation of atheism, supporting his argument by reference to Newton. The latter's letters in reply are of special interest and will be mentioned again later.

The first edition of the *Principia* was sold out by 1691, but from a letter to Flamsteed in August of that year in which he introduces David Gregory, Newton evidently did not contemplate an immediate revision of his work. Asking Flamsteed for observations of Jupiter and Saturn for the next few years, Newton adds: "If you and I live not long enough, Mr. Gregory and Mr. Halley are young men."

At this point the strange figure of Fatio de Duillier crosses the stage. His fanatical enthusiasm, first for Leibniz and then for Newton, has already been mentioned. Now his name appears as a possible editor of a second edition of the *Principia*. That Newton entertained the idea seems probable from the contents of a letter dated 14 March, 1693, in which he urged Fatio to come to live at Cambridge:

The chamber next me is disposed of; but that which I was contriving was, that since your want of health would not give you leave to undertake your design for a subsistence at London, to make you such an allowance as might make your subsistence here easy to you. And, if your affairs in Switzerland be not so pressing but that without damage to them you may stay still some time in England (as your last letter gives me hopes), you will much oblige me by returning hither.

Indeed Huygens and Leibniz thought Newton fortunate to have had the offer of Fatio's assistance. But like many enthusiasts, the latter overstepped himself in Newton's estimation when he propounded his own theory of gravity in which he maintained that the weight of a body was due to the pressure of the atmosphere.

It seems that Newton himself began the revision of the *Principia* in 1694, intending to enlarge Book III and include the results of his recent work on lunar theory. His intention apparently became known and at a meeting of the Royal Society in October 1694

a letter from Mr. Leibnitz to Mr. Bridges was produced and read, wherein he recommended to the Society to use their endeavours to induce Mr. Newton to publish his further thoughts and improvements on the subject of his late book *Principia Philosophiae Mathematica*, and his other Physical and Mathematical discoveries, lest by his death they should happen to be lost.

But despite popular appeal Newton confined himself to a revision of the first edition and continued his work privately on gravitational problems. In September 1694 he visited the Astronomer Royal at Greenwich for certain astronomical data. Correspondence with Flamsteed followed; in October, when asking for further observations, Newton wrote that he hoped to " set right the moon's theory this winter"; and in November he adds: " I desire only such observations as tend to the perfecting the theory of the planets in order to a second edition of my book." It may be noted that several factors should be taken into account when estimating responsibility for a certain amount of friction between the two men which arose over the observations already mentioned. Both Newton and Flamsteed were in poor health at the time; Bentley's unfortunate remark that Newton could not get lunar observations by which to check his theory was repeated to Flamsteed; and reflections on Newton's friend Halley appeared in Flamsteed's communications. Unfortunately some ten years later there was further friction between Newton and Flamsteed over the publication of the latter's catalogue of stars.

Enough has been said in this survey to explain delay in the publication of the second edition of the *Principia*. The appointment of Newton as Warden of the Mint in 1696 further complicated matters. It will be seen in the next chapter that although the appointment was made on the assumption that Newton would have sufficient time to continue his scientific studies, in fact the duties of the Mint turned out to be much more onerous than anticipated, especially so in the hands of so conscientious a man as Newton.

According to Rigaud, it was believed that Gregory was to have had the superintendence of the second edition of the *Principia* if his death in 1709 had not prevented it. Rigaud points out that " it was in June 1709 (precisely the year in which he died) that the papers were put into Cotes' hands for this purpose and we are informed that Bentley had long solicited and urged Newton to the undertaking before he could succeed in prevailing on him to engage in it ". Though Cotes at first found progress inevitably slow, later Newton took such interest in the completion of the edition that Rigaud could refer thus to the correspondence amounting to nearly three hundred letters, that it " must afford the most valuable and interesting information of the advances which Newton made from his first brilliant discoveries to the more complete and accurate development of them ".

Bentley played a prominent part in the production of the

second edition. Newton had allowed him to act as editor in 1708, but he gave up this task to Cotes with the concurrence of Newton in 1709, though he maintained the commercial supervision and financial interest in the printing. About half was ready by April 1710 and the whole issue in July 1713—unbound 15*s.*; bound 18*s.* to 21*s.* Probably 750 copies were printed, 200 of which were sent to Holland. The profits were taken by Bentley, and apparently Cotes' only remuneration was a gift of twelve copies of the book. It is recorded that Conduitt asked Newton why he let Bentley print his *Principia*, which he, Bentley, did not understand: the answer was revealing: "he was covetous, and I let him do it to get money."

In contrast, Newton's generosity to Pemberton, when the third edition was issued in 1726, is an indication of the help and encouragement he gave to younger men. In addition to paying him two hundred guineas in acknowledgment of his labours, Newton allowed Pemberton to take the profits of the edition.

Of the history of the *Principia* subsequent to Newton's death, little need be added except to direct attention to Motte's translation into English in 1729 and its re-issue with historical background by Cajori in 1934.

The unfolding of Newton's life and work up to the time of the publication of the *Principia* reveals, not only greatness and originality in his mental powers, but also complexity and contrast in his personal qualities. These are all the more difficult to assess in the light of Newton's unique position as the doyen of British science. It is not surprising that the early biographers, owerawed by the presence of such a master mind, exalted their hero so that criticism of him in any capacity seemed little short of blasphemy. The nineteenth century with its tendency towards extravagant and ornate expression made it easy for writers to indulge in superlatives, so far as praise was concerned, and blindness in relation to human shortcomings.

Among the contrasted qualities in Newton's personality, are those of reticence and boldness. One of the striking characteristics of his work is that he never forced his discoveries on the world. In fact, it was only with difficulty that he was persuaded to make them public. Against this reticence must be set a boldness which no force could curb when once his mind had been set on a definite course of action. This was apparent when Newton was confronted with the change in political and religious outlook which took place on the accession of James II in 1685.

The sympathetic consideration which natural philosophy or science received at the hands of his brother and predecessor Charles II, was apparent in the continued existence of the Royal Society, whose charter was granted by the King in 1662, and in the Royal Observatory, which Charles founded at Greenwich in 1675. Less spectacular was the help that Newton received from Charles II in connection with his College Fellowship, when his income had every prospect of being reduced. Before his election to the chair of astronomy as Lucasian professor, he had received some financial assistance from his mother, but it is not likely that this was continued with her increasing responsibility for the three children of her second marriage. The Fellowship at Trinity College could only be renewed if Newton entered Holy Orders. This he was not prepared to do: from his theological writings, which will be considered later, it would seem that Newton preferred freedom of thought untrammelled by subscription to a particular creed. Without Royal intervention the Fellowship would have been forfeit, so Newton accordingly made an application to the King for a dispensation allowing him to retain the Fellowship as a layman and as Lucasian professor; the petition was granted. Charles II had also had personal knowledge of Newton's reflecting telescope, having examined it and expressed his admiration when, in 1671, it had been sent to London at the request of the Royal Society.

On the death of Charles II in 1685, religion and state underwent considerable strain. The new monarch's Roman Catholic sympathies found expression in attempts to favour his co-religionists despite the existence of laws preventing their occupying certain posts. Whatever might be argued concerning the relation of the head of the state to the national church, there could be little doubt that, so far as the universities were concerned, the King had no prerogative. A university is a living and corporate body of those whose aim is the furtherance and dissemination of knowledge. Degrees are awarded by a university in relation to a standard set up by the corporate body itself. A university would clearly be failing in its whole purpose if it allowed any outside interference with its academic freedom or condoned any lowering of its agreed standards.

The first clash came at Oxford, where the University was forced by James II to accept, as Dean of Christ Church—a position of high academic status—a man who had no qualification for the post, but who was a Roman Catholic. In February 1687 it was the turn of Cambridge. The Vice-Chancellor received a letter under His Majesty's sign manual to the effect that having heard much in commendation of one Alban Francis, a Benedictine, "the King was pleased to command the University that they should admit him to the degree of Master of Arts without administering to him any oath or oaths: whatsoever any law or statute to the contrary in any wise notwithstanding with which His Majesty was pleased graciously to dispense in behalf of the said Alban Francis." To members of the present

generation who have lived in and value an atmosphere of toler-
ance in every walk of life, the royal mandate might perhaps
appear a trivial request. But the actions of any age must be
judged in relation to the atmosphere and conditions of the lives
of the men and women of the time. In the seventeenth century
the Protestant way of worship was regarded as a vital heritage—freedoms which were jealously guarded by Act of
Parliament. The change from absolute toward constitutional
monarchy had been gradual, but none the less real, and no
King of England could, without serious opposition, arbitrarily
alter laws which had been based on the expressed will of the
people.

At the time when the King's mandate was received at Cambridge, Newton had been engaged on the final stages in the
publication of the *Principia*. On the surface, it would hardly
appear likely that a university professor, pre-occupied with the
preparation of a work which modern science has acknowledged
as its corner-stone, would take an active interest, or play an
important part in resisting the demands of James II. Yet here
is the paradox of reticence and boldness in Newton's character.
The fact that an appreciable part of his life was devoted to
national affairs is indeed surprising in view of his concentration
on mathematical problems of the Universe. One does not
expect the writer of a book such as the *Principia* to spend the
second half of his life in responsible public administration. It
is worth while therefore to trace some of the influences that
made this possible.

Responsibility and family tradition in the affairs of the
manor of Woolsthorpe were not lost on Newton; in fact he took
considerable interest in tracing his own lineage. But apart from
the heritage of the past there is another factor that must have
stimulated his interest in matters of state. This was his friendship with Charles Montague (1661–1715), later Earl of Halifax,
Chancellor of the Exchequer and President of the Royal
Society. In fact, in a letter written to Halley in February 1686
Newton refers to his "intimate friend Mr. C. Montague".

Dr Halley

Orbells buildings in Kensington
March 1st 172⅘.

I thank you for the Table you sent me of the motion
of the Comet of 1680 in a Parabolic Orb so as to answer to
Kirks Observations as well as to Flamsteed's. It answers all their
Observations well enough for my purpose. But you have
omitted the distances of the Comet from the Sun in parts of the
mean distance of the earth from the Sun divided into 100000
equal parts: such parts as the Latus rectum of this Parabolic
Orb consists of 2508. These distances you have computed
already in your papers in wch you calculated this Table, & you
need only to copy them from thence. I have inclosed a copy
of your Table with a vacant column for these distances,
& beg the favour of you to fill it up by inserting these distances out of those your loos papers in wch you made your
calculations of this Table. The distances are inserted in
your Table published in the second edition of my Principles
pag 459. I intend still to keep that Table & add this new
one to it if you please to fill up the column of distances in
the same manner that the two Tables may be like one another.
And by the help of this new Table I shall be able to make the
schemes of the motion of this Comet more perfect. I am

Yor humble servant
Isaac Newton.

Letter to Halley, March 1724/5 [see *Notes on the Illustrations*]

Badge for Stone's Foundation
[see page 149]

Reflecting telescope made by Newton
[see *Notes on the Illustrations*]

Newton's association with Montague began at Cambridge. Charles Montague was born the year Newton went up to Trinity College and so was his junior by nineteen years. A grandson of the first Earl of Manchester, he was educated at Westminster School where he was elected a King's Scholar, and entered Trinity College as a Fellow Commoner in 1679 and as such would be likely to meet Newton, then a Fellow of the College. In 1681 Montague received the degree of M.A. by royal mandate. Although devoted to literary studies, he became a friend of Newton and was so interested in natural philosophy that he co-operated with the latter in an attempt in 1685 to establish a Philosophical Society at Cambridge. The plan failed as there were not enough persons interested in carrying out experiments. But the year 1685 also led to the appearance of Montague within the precincts of the Royal Court. In that year King Charles II died and Montague's literary talents enabled him to compose an ode which began:

> Farewell, Great Charles, Monarch of Blest Renown,
> The best Good Man that ever fill'd a Throne:

This and other popular writing led to the Earl of Dorset becoming his patron and bringing him to the notice of the reigning monarch, who gave orders that a pension of five hundred pounds be paid to Montague out of the Privy Purse until an opportunity should occur of giving him an appointment.

The friendship which Newton mentioned in his letter to Halley was so real that it could not fail to influence and enlarge Newton's interest in the political problems which soon came to a head in the short years of James II's reign, namely 1685-88.

But Newton's emergence from the seclusion of the student to the publicity of the man of affairs must have been due, in addition to any influence of Montague, to his own attributes and love for the defence of freedom. Surely for no other reason would the Senate of the University, when James II thrust upon them his mandate concerning Father Alban Francis, have included Newton in the deputation which was ultimately summoned to appear before the High Commission at Westminster in April 1687. Before leaving Cambridge, the deputation held a meeting to decide on their course of action. The Chancellor of Ely supported a proposal to grant the degree to Francis on the condition that it should not create a precedent. When the Chancellor produced a paper for the others to sign in support of the proposal, there seemed to be general assent; but, according to a MS. of Conduitt, Newton, realising the seriousness of the compromise, rose from his chair, took two or three turns round the room, and addressing the University bedell (archaic form of " beadle ", an officer of a university or law-court, whose duties include leading a ceremonial procession) then standing at the fire, said to him, " this is giving up the question." " So it is," replied the bedell. " Why didn't you go and speak to it? " Whereupon Newton went to the table, expressed his opinion, and proposed that the paper be shown to counsel. The suggestion was adopted. Mr. Finch, a solicitor, was consulted and as a result Newton's opinion was upheld and the rest of the deputation concurred.

The formalities of the reception of the deputation at Westminster need not detain us. On 7 May, 1687, the case was defended, though not forcefully, by the Vice-Chancellor of the University, who headed the deputation. The argument against the Crown was based on the fact that during the reign of Charles II several royal mandates had been withdrawn, and that no degree had ever been confirmed without the oath of supremacy and obedience being taken. The president of the court, Judge Jeffreys, of the 1685 " Bloody Assize ", with characteristic insolence denounced the timid Vice-Chancellor, silenced the other members of the deputation when they offered to speak, and without a hearing, ordered them all out of Court. When the deputation was recalled, the members were reprimanded and the Vice-Chancellor deprived of the office and emoluments as Master of Magdalene College. Jeffreys closed his address with the words: " Therefore I shall say to you what the Scripture says, and rather because most of you are divines, ' Go your way and sin no more, lest a worse thing come unto you '." And so Newton went his way—back to Cambridge, back to the *Principia*, for which his name stands for ever as one of the great benefactors of mankind: his protagonist has gone down in history as the epitome of the bully.

In Chapter II, attention was directed to the significance of the so-called Glorious Revolution of 1688–89. In the light of Newton's advocacy of a bold policy in dealing with the "Alban Affair" and thus guarding the privileges of the University, it is no wonder that his friends deemed him a suitable candidate to represent the University in Parliament. The voting for two seats is of interest in view of the third candidate, whose name has already been mentioned: Sir Robert Sawyer 125, Mr. Newton 122, Mr. Finch 117. Some of the voting papers in support of Newton added Latin epithets denoting integrity or learning. And so, with the confidence of his colleagues, Newton was elected to the "Convention Parliament" which in 1689 welcomed William and Mary as King and Queen after the ignominious flight of James II.

It was not long before Newton's good offices showed themselves in advice to the Vice-Chancellor of Cambridge. Despite the determined and successful stand which the University had made against the despotism of James II in the matter of Father Alban Francis, there were signs that some members wavered at the advent of William and Mary. They felt on grounds of conscience that having already sworn allegiance to their predecessor, they could not lightly transfer their fidelity to the new monarchs. On 12 February, 1689, the day after William and Mary were proclaimed at Whitehall, Newton intimated to the Vice-Chancellor that he would receive an order to proclaim them at Cambridge. Enclosing a form of the proclamation, Newton heartily expressed "the wish that the University would so compose themselves as to perform the solemnity with a reasonable decorum; because I take it to be their interest to set the best face upon things as they can, after the example of the London Divines".

During Newton's residence in London as a member of Parliament, he became acquainted with John Locke in 1689, and later in the same year he met Christian Huygens at a meeting of the Royal Society.

The Convention Parliament was short-lived, for in February 1690 it was dissolved. The Tories obtained a majority in the new House of Commons and Newton had foreseen that there would be no chance of his re-election. In fact he returned to Cambridge two days before the Dissolution and once more took up his former scholarly role. About this time Newton showed an increasing interest in theology, stimulated no doubt by his discussions with Locke on the doctrine of the Trinity and on the prophecies. The esteem in which Newton was held led his friends to influence the King to issue a *mandamus* to appoint him Provost of King's College, Cambridge, but as he was not in Holy Orders or a Fellow of the College, the application failed. In 1691 Newton himself would not agree to a suggestion that he should become Master of Charterhouse. Locke drew from him the reply that he saw nothing in the situation worth

making a bustle for. Besides a coach which I consider not, 'tis but £200 per annum, with a confinement to the London Air, and to such a way of living as I am not in love with, neither do I think it advisable to enter into such a competition as that would be for a better place.

By 1693 Newton seems to have felt that his friends were not doing enough in his interest, and indeed he was suspicious that Montague was proving false. In addition to this sense of frustration Newton experienced a sorrow, in the death of his mother, which because of his devotion to her must have been in the nature of a calamity. He had left all his engagements to nurse her, but despite every care and attention she did not recover from a fever which she had caught from her son Benjamin Smith, Newton's step-brother. The depressing effect on Newton of her death was the more keenly felt as he had been in the habit of visiting Woolsthorpe frequently. Another loss which must have had a considerable effect on Newton's outlook occurred soon after the publication of the *Principia*, in the death of his friend Henry More of Christ's College, Cambridge.

With the mental strain of completing the *Principia*, and the stress of personal bereavement, with loss of sleep and neglect of proper and regular nourishment, it is not surprising that these factors combined to cause such nervous exhaustion that Newton's friends became anxious for his health. In the last chapter mention was made of the friction between Newton and Flamsteed, which was aggravated by the indifferent health of both. Rumour is ever ready to exaggerate the sensational and this is well illustrated in a reference by Huygens in 1694 to a derangement in Newton's mind caused either from too great application to his studies, or from excessive grief at having lost by fire his chemical laboratory and some papers. On referring to Newton's illness in a letter to Leibniz, the latter replied, " I am very happy that I received information of the cure of Mr. Newton, at the same time that I first heard of his illness, which without doubt, must have been most alarming. It is to men like Newton and yourself, sir, that I desire health and a long life." This is dated 23 June, 1694.

The fire in Newton's room referred to by Huygens has already been mentioned in Chapter V: it is associated with a dog, Diamond, which is supposed to have caused the fire by upsetting a lighted candle and which on Newton's return to his room received no stripe, but reproach in an appropriately fictitious phrase: "Oh, Diamond! Diamond! thou little knowest the mischief done! " The story, based perhaps on a fire that did occur, grew out of all proportion and would make good conversation about a professor in the undergraduate world of that day, as indeed it would today.

From his letters to Pepys and Locke in September 1693, it would appear that Newton was on the verge of a serious mental collapse. In his own words written from Cambridge to Locke on 5 October of the same year, we have a glimpse of the cause of the disturbance.

The last winter, by sleeping too often by my fire, I got an ill habit of sleeping: and a distemper, which this summer has been epidemical, put me farther out of order, so that when I wrote to you, I had not slept an hour a night for a fortnight together, and for five nights together not a wink. I remember I wrote to you, but what I said of your book I remember not. If you please to send me a transcript of that passage, I will give you an account of it if I can.

Do not the symptoms find an echo in many a case of nervous strain in the twentieth century? L. T. More in his biography of Newton collects, sifts and weighs the evidence and expresses the opinion that Newton recovered entirely his health by the end of the year; and that the last letters to Pepys and to Locke show that he had realised his condition, and his apologies express a pathetic humility for his unwarranted attacks on them. More points out that we hear of no more trouble, and the only permanent effect of his illness was a certain lassitude of mind and unwillingness to engage in creative work. Tribute should especially be paid to John Locke, whose magnanimity, good-humoured forbearance, respect and affection did so much to restore his friend, at a time when personal understanding was so vital.

Even the casual observer must be impressed by one aspect of Newton's illness—namely, that it preceded the second half of his career, to which mental alertness combined with administrative efficiency were essential attributes. It must always be a source of wonder that, first as Warden and later as Master of the Mint, this man of science could also be the man of public affairs.

The present imposing building on Tower Hill, in the heart of London, dating from 1811 and known as the Royal Mint, stands in sharp contrast to the series of wooden structures between the outer and inner walls of the Tower of London which, at the time of Newton, housed the Mint. Even more marked is the modern central system of administration based on the metropolis in place of provincial mints, each producing coins in different parts of the realm. Very different, too, was the Treasury background of the seventeenth century from that of the twentieth. In addition, although the London Mint had been guaranteed its independence, the military requirements of Charles II, and the consequent expansion of the garrison of the Tower, resulted in an overflow into the private domain of the Mint, even to building barracks on vacant land. The whole area included about twenty dwellings, workshops, stores, stables, coach-houses, and at one end the Irish Mint extension built by Elizabeth I for coinage in that country. At night four oil lamps lit the road through the Mint and sentries patrolled it. Although intended as a security measure, the sentries were posted singly, with but little guarantee of their integrity, especially with the temptation to pilfer so obviously at hand.

The old methods of coining by hand and hammer were superseded in 1662 by mechanical presses, trials of which had been made since the latter part of the sixteenth century. According to Newton, a coin could be struck every two seconds; but the strain on the labourers operating the press was so great that they were able to work only fifteen minutes at a time. It had been anticipated that the new processes would provide a practically perfect coinage, but events proved otherwise. Once again in the story of progress, the weaknesses of human nature thwarted the ideals of those who planned. The result was that the silver circulation became divided into two—the new coins which were used for savings, export, or melting down for bullion, and the old which continued in circulation. The latter gradually became more and more debased by wear and tear. Above all, at the hands of the unscrupulous, the silver coins suffered by filing and snipping of the better specimens, to obtain silver. The practice of course was not new, but about 1686 it flared up to such an extent that an illicit trade, in which respectable bankers joined, ruined the coinage. Counterfeits and foreign imitations added to the confusion and general distrust. Then came inflation, following the new system of credit and the expensive wars on the Continent, which began when, in the third year of his reign, William led British troops across the sea. Matters reached a climax when some people not only lost confidence in the currency, but also linked its weakness with the change in kingship from James II to William and Mary.

The day of the professional economist had not yet dawned and remedies were proffered by amateurs in varied walks of life, their opinions being asked in their capacity as men of commerce. From his professorial chair at Cambridge, Newton, with characteristic practical and systematic outlook, maintained that the face value of the silver coin must be brought in line with the market price of bullion. There is something of a modern ring about his suggestion that a Price Control Board should be established for the period of the war. Christopher Wren advocated a decimal system of coinage. John Locke recommended that the worn coins should be kept in circulation but reduced in value by about half. The measures ultimately accepted by Parliament were, however, laid down by Charles Montague, then Chancellor of the Exchequer, and involved the withdrawal of all handstruck coins without change of standards, provided they were handed in within a limited time.

So came about the Great Recoinage. It has been severely criticised by modern economists, and despite the credit given to Newton for the measures, it is only fair to point out that the principles underlying it were not advocated by him. Indeed the necessary legislation had been passed, the proclamations published and some of the new coins issued and more of the old collected before he came to the Mint.

G. M. Trevelyan maintains that the great achievement of the Whig ministers was the institution of the modern system of finance with which England has since fought all her great wars of European security and colonial expansion. The Bank of England was established (1694) in connection with the National Debt, against the opposition of the Tories, who were jealous of the monied interest. A regular method of Government borrowing was thus set up, which enabled a King who could not tax his subjects at will, to outlast in resources a despot whose subjects had but little left for him to take. Concerning these measures and the task of recoinage (1696) Trevelyan writes:

The Whig leaders of the rising generation, Somers and Montague, in close consultation with the Whig philosophers, Newton and Locke, effected these great measures, which they had devised by their own science and wisdom, and carried through by the strength of party spirit in the City and the House of Commons. Under this new leadership, the wisdom of the Whigs saved the State which had been so often shaken by their folly.

It is significant comment that one who, at the time of writing the above was Professor of Modern History in the University of Cambridge, should thus name Newton and Locke together as advisers to such statesmen as Montague and Somers. The extract gives colour to the opinion expressed earlier that Newton, by the time the *Principia* was published, and then forty-five years of age, was becoming a man of national stature in the political affairs of the country.

There is no need to follow in detail the repercussions of Montague's monetary policy. The loss to the Treasury and to private individuals has been estimated at £5,000,000, which represented more than a year's revenue of the Government. Riots and commercial crises followed, and compelled the Bank of England to stop payments. For the present purpose it is sufficient to emphasise that Newton was not responsible for the policy but only for its implementation so far as the Mint was concerned.

Reference has just been made to John Locke and his attitude to the nation's problems. In 1691 he tried unsuccessfully to secure Newton's presence at the Mint, but it was not until March 1696 that Montague, who was then Chancellor of the

Exchequer and President of the Royal Society, wrote to the most distinguished of its Fellows:

I am very glad that at last I can give you a good proof of my friendship and the esteem the King has of your merits. Mr. Overton, the Warden of the Mint, is made one of the Commissioners of the Customs and the King has promised me to make Mr. Newton Warden of the Mint, the office is the most proper for you, 'tis the Chief Officer in the Mint, 'tis worth five or six hundred pounds p. An., and has not too much bus'ness to require more attendance than you may spare. . . .

The remuneration was overstated as the Warden's salary was £400, but Newton accepted. His appointment under the Privy Seal is dated 13 April and he took the oath to keep secret the edging apparatus on 2 May. The appointment allowed him to retain his Fellowship at Trinity College and the post of Lucasian Professor of Mathematics in the University of Cambridge.

Thus began a part of Newton's career which covers some thirty years of his life. The year 1696 marks his final departure from Cambridge, from the seclusion of his rooms in Trinity Great Court to the business and bustle of London, first in the Minories near the Mint, then by the autumn of 1696 in Jermyn Street about two miles away.

There are not many happenings in the daily life of an individual of the seventeenth century about which one may write with certainty. But to a resident in Jermyn Street, as Newton was in 1698, the fire which destroyed the Palace of Whitehall must have caused excitement and consternation that would linger in the memory for many a day. The terseness of the entry in Evelyn's *Diary* for 5 January, 1697–8, makes the incident all the more poignant: "Whitehall burnt: nothing but walls and ruins left." It was believed at the time that a Dutch laundress (who probably crossed from Holland in the service of William of Orange) carelessly lit a fire in an upper room to dry some linen and left it unattended. The contemporary account of what happened is preserved in the Annals of the Wren Society and it concludes " It is a dismal sight to behold such a glorious, famous, and much renowned palace reduced to a heap of rubbish and ashes, which the day before might justly contend with any palace in the world for riches, nobility, honour and grandeur."

The importance of Whitehall as the centre of English life would be well appreciated by Newton on his journeys to London, whether for meetings of the Royal Society, for the summons to appear with other Cambridge officials before Judge Jeffreys, or taking his seat as a Member of the Convention Parliament. After he settled in Jermyn Street in 1696, Newton must have been especially familiar with the Whitehall area, the fringe of which he would traverse on his daily journeys to the Mint.

To understand the part that Whitehall played in the nation's life reference must be made to its origin. In 1529 Henry VIII confiscated York Place which was the London residence of Cardinal Wolsey, Archbishop of York, until his downfall. Shakespeare makes reference to the alteration in name in *Henry VIII* (Act IV, Sc. 1):

> Sir,
> You must no more call it York Place; that's past:
> For since the Cardinal fell, that title's lost;
> 'Tis now the King's and called Whitehall.

But it was under the Stuarts that Whitehall achieved its greatest fame. Though James I's elaborate ideas for a new palace did not materialise, the fine Banqueting Hall of Inigo Jones (1573–1652) which was begun in 1619, may still be seen. After the Fire of 1698 the Banqueting Hall was the only landmark that remained of the numerous buildings of the Royal Palace. Amongst those that were destroyed was the nearby Chapel Royal situated on the site of the present Horse Guards' Avenue. Henry Purcell (1659–1695) was a chorister at the Chapel Royal until 1673, and later organist of Westminster Abbey from 1679 until his death. He was succeeded by his former master John Blow (*c.* 1648–1708), a foremost English Church musician who composed several anthems for various special occasions. These included the Coronation of James II in 1685, that of William and Mary in 1689, the opening of St. Paul's Cathedral as rebuilt by Wren in 1697 and the Thanksgiving for the victory of Blenheim in 1704. In view of Newton's increasing public activities, he would be present in an official capacity at many of these functions.

With the destruction of Whitehall the Court had to move elsewhere and indeed William III, who suffered from asthma, had, previously to the Fire, resided at Kensington (where Newton retired later on the grounds of health). From the time of Queen Anne the monarch lived at St. James's Palace; Buckingham Palace did not become the London residence of the Sovereign until the accession of Queen Victoria in 1837.

Most biographies of Newton pass briefly over the long years spent at the Mint, due in part no doubt to the fact that until after the Second World War, certain of Newton's important papers relating to the Mint were inaccessible. As Sir John Craig writes in the Preface to his book *Newton at the Mint*, published in 1946:

Newton's monetary theories were examined in an article by Professor Shirras and myself in the *Economic Journal* for June 1945, but without access to his recommendations for the Great Recoinage, then hidden beneath the tide of war. On this point also the previously accepted account must be reversed.

On his arrival at the Mint, Newton found the senior officers disunited and self-seeking: he was thus faced with a human problem as well as that of the recoinage, which had already started. As a matter of principle, Newton approached the Treasury to adjust his own position as Warden so that it was commensurate with the increasing responsibilities of an expanding Mint. The conversion of bars of raw material into coins had by long usage been the responsibility of the Company of Moneyers, descended from the old guild of coiners. At the time of the recoinage the garrison had been thrust back into the Tower, melting facilities had been enlarged, some machines doubled, others trebled. By May 1693, the Moneyers had increased their horses to 33 and their men to 160 and later to 500. This of course was done before Newton arrived and in any event did not fall to the lot of the Warden. One of his first duties was the appointment of deputies at each of the five provincial Mints. Newton does not seem to have used his influence in appointing his own friends, as Edmond Halley was made Deputy Comptroller at Chester by someone else.

In June 1697 discipline had so deteriorated at Chester that one officer challenged another to a duel. Newton is probably responsible for the following official rebuke:

We are much concerned to hear of your continued quarrels . . . we believe both sides much in the wrong and resolve to come and hear it ourselves. . . . Till we come let there be no further quarrelling . . . for the Mint will not allow of the drawing of swords and assaulting of any, nor ought such language we hear has been, be used any more amongst you.

At Norwich the Deputy Master of the Mint had all his property confiscated and spent several years in prison. The Deputy Comptroller at Exeter had still not cleared his accounts when, according to Sir John Craig, he died whilst holding his next appointment as "Ambassador to the Pirates of Madagascar"!

Nor was Newton free from indiscipline at the Mint itself. Late in June 1697 an inebriated officer of the garrison attempted to break into a Mint residence and attack the householder. A sentry refused assistance, and musketeers were summoned from within the Tower. Lord Lucas, Lieutenant of the Tower, ultimately gave orders that his sentries should fire on the drunk and disorderly. "A bloody discipline," was Newton's comment, ". . . why should the people who live in the Mint be so terrified as to leave their habitations in it?" Newton was unsuccessful in a personal appeal to Lucas, and considerable friction—and at times riot—amongst the Mint workers and soldiers ensued, lasting to the end of Newton's tenure of office.

Newton's handling of the case of William Challoner is further evidence of his firmness in dealing with human nature. In 1696 the House of Commons appointed a Committee of

Inquiry into abuses at the Mint, Newton was the official witness on administration and duties. Among hostile witnesses was one, William Challoner. He had already published a pamphlet in 1695: *Reasons humbly offered against passing an Act for raising £1,000,000 for making good the deficiency of the Clipt-Money*. In February 1696, he approached the Privy Council and Montague concerning the incompetence of the Mint, claiming for himself a better method of coining. He gave evidence that the Mint made counterfeit coin and was in fact in league with counterfeiters. In short, he could put matters right. Newton refused the Committee's request that Challoner should demonstrate with the Mint machines, maintaining they were secret; but he did carry out tests in the Mint which showed that Challoner's ideas were not practicable.

On Newton's authority, Challoner was put in irons in Newgate prison; he justified his action on the ground that the prisoner was about to commit another felony. Newton continued his allegations before a Parliamentary inquiry in 1698 and gave the life history of Challoner. This is told by Craig in the following extract, based on Newton's manuscripts:

Seven years before, he (Challoner) had been but a poor workman in the new trade of japanning; a career of crime had raised him to the dignity of a residence in Kensington, a dinner service of plate and the clothes of a gentleman. Challoner had become the most accomplished counterfeiter in the kingdom of English or foreign coin; an inventor of better ways of casting and moulding; so nice an artist of dies that it galled him to spoil their perfection by use. As sidelines, he had stolen horses to furnish capital for a coiner's headquarters in the country; £200 had been obtained from the Bank of England for information about a forgery of their documents; the Exchequer had been robbed of £1,000 by an elaborate trick. This sum had been offered by the Government for betrayal of the source of propaganda which was being spread about London on behalf of James II. Challoner got hold of a copy of the objectionable circular, had forty more copies printed, informed on the printers and pocketed the cash. And, dog eating dog, he had also sent a fellow false coiner to the scaffold.

The true intent of his appearance before the Committee of Miscarriages [Craig continues] had been to coax out of them an appointment within the Mint, as a help to making flash coin outside it.

Challoner was overthrown—no mean achievement for a don pitted against a clever criminal, with hostile politicians as jury. He was convicted of false coining, drawn on a sledge to Tyburn and executed on 4 March, 1699, and would have been hanged long before had he not turned King's evidence. Newton ran the prosecution.

It is clear that the limits of this chapter will not permit even a rough recital of Newton's work and reforms at the Mint; but the case of Challoner has been given in some detail to direct attention to the revealing nature of the material that has but recently been made available. Newton is as much of an enigma at the Mint as at Cambridge. In spite of his preoccupation with his duties as Warden and Master of the Mint, he still found time to continue his interest in what was known in those days as natural philosophy.

An accepted custom among mathematicians of different countries was for one of them to challenge the rest to solve a particular problem put forward by himself as challenger. A remarkable case is the speed with which Newton solved the well-known problem of the *brachistochrone* (Greek: *brachistos*-shortest, *chronos*-time), set by John Bernoulli (1667-1748), a member of a distinguished family of Swiss mathematicians. The problem may be stated thus:

Given two points A and B, such that the straight line joining them is neither horizontal nor vertical, to find how the curve joining them must be drawn, so that if a particle starts from the top end and falls along the curve under gravity it shall reach the lower end in the least possible time.

A related problem was also included. The challenge reached Newton on 29 January, 1697, and the sequel is best described in a note made by Newton's niece: " 1697, Bernoulli sent problem.—I.N. home at 4 p.m.—finished it by 4 a.m." So on

The First Book

Concerning the Language of the Prophets

Chap 1

A Synopsis of the Prophetick figures

He that would understand a book written in a strange language, must first learn the language. & if he would understand it well he must learn the language perfectly. Such a language as that wherein the Prophets wrote, & the want of sufficient skill in that language is the main reason why they are so little understood. John did not write in one language, Daniel in another, Isaiah in a third & the rest in others peculiar to themselves, but they all wrote in one & the same mystical language, as well known without doubt to the sons of the Prophets as the Hieroglyphick language of the Egyptians to their Priests. And this language so far as I can find was as certain & definite in its signification as is the vulgar language of any nation whatsoever so that it is only through want of skill therein that Interpreters so frequently turn the Prophetick types & phrases to signify whatever their fansies & hypotheses lead them to. He therefore that would understand the old Prophets (as all Divines ought to do) must first find the significations of their types & phrases in the beginning of his studies. Some thing in this kind has been done by former writers: & as I have endeavoured in the following discourse to carry on the designe further, so I hope others will bring it to more perfection. The Rule I have followed has been to compare

Roubiliac's statue of Newton, in the Ante-Chapel, Trinity College, Cambridge

the day after receiving the challenge, solutions to both problems were sent to Montague, who was then President of the Royal Society. Some sympathy may be felt for the late eighteenth-century writer who preferred the simpler name *cycloid*; " curve of a cycloid, which was afterwards called by the hard name of a brachistochrone, or the line of quickest descent."

A letter from Newton to Flamsteed in January 1699, refusing to have a reference to his inquiries into the moon's orbit published, is characteristic: " I do not love to be printed on every occasion . . . or to be thought by our own people to be trifling my time about them (*sc.* mathematical problems) when I should be about the King's business." About the same year Newton put forward the rival claims of the Julian and Gregorian Calendars, together with a suggestion of his own dividing the year at the equinoxes and solstices into six winter months of 30 days, five summer months of 31 days and one summer month of 30 days which became 31 in leap year. Newton's work on the reform of the calendar ran into thousands of words; but he did not think that the number of days in a month should be altered " without the consent of a good part of Europe ". As further evidence of his general interest in scientific matters while at the Mint it may be mentioned that in August 1699 he exhibited to the Royal Society a sextant which he had constructed; no serious use was made of this. It was left to Hadley in 1730 to re-invent it, and his name is perpetuated in the description *Hadley's Sextant*.

The Master of the Mint, Thomas Neale, died at the end of the year 1699; Newton succeeded him on Boxing Day, 26 December, the day after his forty-seventh birthday, and so became responsible for the administration of the Mint. It was unusual for the Warden to receive this promotion, and the obvious reason would be Newton's integrity and efficiency. A romantic explanation has also been put forward and was taken up much later by Voltaire. It has to do with Newton's niece, Catherine Barton, for whom Montague, then Lord Halifax, and at the time of Newton's first appointment, Lord Treasurer, had much regard. But there is much against the idea of Lord Halifax using his influence to get such an appointment for Newton, in order to win his niece. Catherine was only fifteen years old in 1696, and there is no reason to believe that Montague, who was not then a widower, had ever seen her. At the time of Newton's appointment as Master of the Mint, Montague and the Whigs were no longer in the ascendancy. Further, Catherine did not keep house for Montague until much later: in 1700 she was living at her uncle's, as the following affectionate letter from Newton shows, and she was at the time recuperating from smallpox.

> *To Mrs. Catherine Barton*
> *at Mr. Gyre's at Pudlicot*
> *near Woodstock, in Oxfordshire*
>
> London, Aug 5, 1700
>
> Dear Niece,
> I had your two letters and am glad the air agrees with you; and although the fever is loth to leave you, yet I hope it abates and that the remains of the smallpox are dropping off apace. Sir Joseph Tilley is leaving Mr. Toll's house, and it's probable I may succeed him. I intend to send you some wine by the next carrier, which I beg the favour of Mr. Gyre and his lady to accept. My Lady Norris thinks you forget your promise to write her, and wants a letter from you. Pray let me know by the next how your face is, and if the fever be going. Perhaps warm milk from the cow may help to abate it.
> I am your very loving uncle
> *Is. Newton.*

It is certain that Catherine brought the letter back to Newton's house in Jermyn Street, for Newton ultimately used the back of it to draft a report to the Treasury. Montague was impeached on a trumped-up political charge in 1701 and was not free of his troubles until 1706; he was then appointed a Commissioner for negotiating the Union with Scotland. Probably at that time Catherine went to superintend Montague's house until his death in 1715.

Newton's mathematical training enabled him to express ideas

exactly and must have stood him in good stead when drafting bills or clauses for the Mint and in other legislation. He had the power of exploiting to the full the nicer meaning of words, and from what has already been said of his relations with Treasury and other officials, it is not surprising that the former found him on occasion a tireless adversary, as well as a most reliable and conscientious custodian of the Mint. The modern distinction between Civil Service and elective offices dates from a little later than Newton's day, so that although he had been defeated in the election following the Convention Parliament, he was able to stand successfully as a member for the University of Cambridge in February 1701. After the dissolution of Parliament in July 1702 he wrote: "I have served you in this Parliament; other gentlemen may expect their turn in the next." These sentiments however did not prevent Newton coming forward as a candidate at the election of 1705, when the Whigs secured only a small majority, but he was defeated in his bid to stand again for Cambridge University.

Newton's responsibilities outside the Mint cannot be given in detail; but they varied from acting as Treasurer, or Auditor, of the Thomas à Beckett Charity in Golden Square, London, to challenging the assessment of his property at Twyford for the payment of rates for relief of the poor and for maintenance of highways. The challenge turned on a technical point concerning the situation of Twyford in the Parish of Colsterworth, which was in the Soke of Grantham; but Twyford was not considered to be in that Soke (originally a legal right over persons only, later it included estates as well as men living on them). So if the property was to be assessed at all, it should be done by the Constable of Colsterworth and not by the Constable of Witham and the Justices of Kesteven.

Newton's professional opinions have sometimes a modern ring:

'Tis mere opinion that sets a value upon money; we value it because with it we can purchase all sorts of commodities, and the same opinion sets a like value upon paper security. . . . All the difference is that value of gold and silver is set upon their internal substance or matter and therefore is called intrinsic, and the value of paper security upon the apparent form of the writing and therefore called extrinsic, and that the value of the former is more universal than that of the latter. . . . Our silver must go to China till gold is dearer there or cheaper with us. And it is our interest to let it go thither. For China is inclined to take off our manufactures which India is not, and therefore is fit to be traded with and the trade for their gold must greatly increase our coin, being a profit to the nation as to the merchant himself.

In September 1701, at the request of the Treasury, Newton made a comprehensive survey, extending over nine months, of the coins of Europe up to the Russian frontier, including at times American, Turkish and even Scots money. Once more, how evident is the contrast between this matter-of-fact man of the world, expressing considered opinions on finance and international relations, and the unobtrusive researches of the Fellow of Trinity College and Lucasian Professor of Mathematics in the University of Cambridge! Newton gave up his University posts in 1701, having passed on the pay of the Lucasian professorship to his successor, Whiston, from the beginning of the year.

Reference, though brief, must be made to Newton's interest in the actual design of special medals whether commemorative of military or naval victories, or of such events as the Coronation of Queen Anne who had succeeded to the throne in 1702, the Union with Scotland of 1707, and the accession of George I in 1714. Newton's sketches are among his MSS. and his knowledge of classical literature may be recognised in the following comment by Craig:

The Master showed a scholarly interest in medal design. The drawing for the Coronation Medal was supported by an erudite, if laboured, exposition of its mythological symbolism. One may doubt whether a committee of statesmen was likely to be moved by the accumulation of quotations from Ovid, Nicander, Philostratus, Isacius, Q. Smyrnaeus, Virgil, Flaccus Argonauticus and St. Matthew.

Particulars of another medal are to be found in E. H. Pearce's *Annals of Christ's Hospital*. This medal, or badge, was worn by boys of the Henry Stone Foundation, a benefaction which helped to supplement Charles II's original endowment for the Royal Mathematical School within Christ's Hospital. This School prepared boys for apprenticeship at sea, and is not only a tribute to the interest of the King in mathematical training for navigation, but also an indication of the current demand for a mathematical education. The provision of officers adequately qualified in navigation had become an urgent necessity in view of England's expanding maritime commitments. The die for the distinguishing badge worn by boys of Stone's Foundation was given by Newton. It bears the name of the founder, Henry Stone, and the legend "*Numero, Pondere et Mensura*". These three aspects: calculation, weighing and mensuration are aptly portrayed by three boys round a table, one, on the left, seated in front of a scroll with figures on it; one, in the centre, standing and holding a balance of the steel-yard type; the third, on the right, bending over the table and using a pair of compasses on another scroll. The dress of the boys is the traditional "blue-coat", characteristic of Christ's Hospital, and the minute detail of the die is in keeping with the care and accuracy which Newton bestowed on all his work.

But Newton's association with the Hospital went much deeper than the presentation of the die, for which the Governors expressed their thanks in 1716. As early as 1682 he was concerned with the appointment of Edward Paget as master of the Mathematical School and, in 1694, with the appointment of his successor. It is interesting comment on the vision of a brilliant band of pioneers, Fellows of the Royal Society, that such men were willing to serve the cause of education by becoming Governors of Christ's Hospital: Newton, Flamsteed, Hooke, Pepys, Locke and Wren—all held this position. About 1694 the advice of the Professors of Mathematics in the Universities of Oxford and Cambridge was sought to revise the curriculum of the Mathematical School. Newton's reply occupies eight closely written pages of the Committee Book; it is interesting and illuminating and may be studied in detail in Eddleston's *Correspondence of Sir Isaac Newton and Professor Cotes, including letters of other eminent men.* This particular letter is dated 25 May, 1694, and accompanying it is *A New Scheme of Learning proposed for the Mathematical Boys in Christ's Hospital.* There are ten articles: the first nine follow Paget's scheme with a few alterations by Newton, but the tenth was added by the latter. It is of special interest, partly in view of its date, only seven years after the publication of the *Principia,* and also because it shows the practical implications of the Newtonian mechanics. For these reasons it is quoted in full:

The principles of reasoning about force and motion, particularly about the five mechanical powers, the stress of ropes and timber, the power of winds, tides, bullets and bombs, according to their velocity and direction against any plane, the line which a bullet describes, the force of weights and springs and the power of fluids to press against imersed bodies, and bear them up, and to resist their motions; with the application of this learning of Sea affairs, for contriving well and managing easily, speedily and dextrously, Levers, Pulleys, Skrews, Anchors, Pumps, Rudders, Guns, Sails and other Tackle, judging truly of the advantages and disadvantages of Vessells, Havens, fforts, Engins and new Projects, and observing or discovering whatever tends to make a Ship endure and Sail well, or otherwise to correct or improve Navigation.

In the letter itself are glimpses of Newton's insight into human nature and its limitations:

A Vulgar Mechanick can practice what he has been taught or seen done, but if he is in error he knows not how to find it out and correct it, and if you put him out of his road, he is at a stand; whereas he that is able to reason nimbly and judiciously about figure, force and motion, is never at rest till he gets over every rub. Experience is necessary, but yet there is the same difference between a mere practical Mechanick and a rational one, as between a mere practical Surveyer or Gager and a good Geometer, of between an Empirick in Physick and a learned and a rational Physitian.

Contrasting adult seamen with the boys of Christ's Hospital, Newton writes of the former: ". . . . whose faculties for learning begin to be as stiff and inflexible as their bones, and whose minds are prepossest and diverted with other things," while of the latter he adds: "children whose parts are Limber and pliable and free to receive all impressions." From the letter also it is evident that Newton realised the claims of other subjects in relation to the study of mathematics and suggests an extra six months training to meet the difficulty, a difficulty which any modern headmaster constantly meets when preparing a school time-table in the face of the conflicting and persistent demands of the specialist members of his staff.

The tin trade in Cornwall seems somewhat removed from Newton's earlier life, when he certainly did not prove a capable overseer of his mother's affairs at Woolsthorpe. On the accession of Queen Anne, Lord Godolphin, who had some interest in Cornwall, developed the idea of a contract between the Queen and the Convention of Tin Miners so that all tin was to be sold to the Queen for seven years. The improved price would have a bearing on the support of the numerous members of Parliament whose constituencies were in the county. A smaller quantity per year was guaranteed for Devon. Hearing that certain subordinate officers at the Mint were planning to make private profits on these transactions, Newton offered in October 1703 to undertake the whole at cost. Sales abroad also came under his jurisdiction. One of Newton's agents was a merchant, Sir Theodore Janssen, who had arranged a specially good paper for the second edition of the *Principia*. The cost and stocks of tin were a source of anxiety to the Mint, and in 1717 the rights reverted to the Prince of Wales and Duke of Cornwall.

Some of Newton's varied interests while at the Mint have already been mentioned, others will find their place more appropriately in the next chapter. Among his professional responsibilities, the recoinage at Edinburgh in connection with the Act of Union brought its own problems. Soldiers were unpaid and the Warden wrote to Newton: "Upon the want of money for carrying on the business of the Mint all the officers of the Mint depend on you very much in this matter . . . for the truth is that the Union has disconcerted our foundation entirely."

The problems of foreign exchange as they affected British soldiers in Dunkirk at the end of Marlborough's wars in 1711 were so complicated that Newton's advice was sought as to how much they should be given in foreign money: but it may be doubted if the private soldier of those days appreciated the presence of a mastermind in his financial affairs! The production of copper coinage for England also revealed Newton's originality—copper which would not crack under a hammer test, when heated to redness, became the specification for coinage copper until the middle of the nineteenth century.

There were two honours which came to Newton during his life in London which reflected the high esteem in which he was held both by his scientific contemporaries and his fellow-countrymen. The first is described in characteristic language by Stukeley:

At length in the fore-part of the present century, he was elected President of the Royal Society (1703). There we view him in his proper dignity. That chair which had held so many great men, his predecessors, was now filled indeed! There he sat at rest, in the intellectual center, as the great solar orb shining with its own light, and diffusing his beamy influence thro' the whole system of arts and sciences. To him gravitated all the lesser lights, both regular planets and extravagant comets of erudition, both at home and abroad, as the moon always turns her face to her principal, the earth. From him they borrow a ray and sip'd from his common fountain; and now was that illustrious body truly so, and at its height of glory, the prototype of these literary Societys in Europe, with the great Newton at their head, as an object almost ador'd. And that great Mecaenas of the learned world, Lewis XIV of France, thought himself honor'd by inlisting Sir Isaac into the number of his beneficiarys. And our countrymen at that time could not have a greater recommendation in foreign parts, nor a freer introduction to the great and the learned, than in quality of that of a member of the Royal Society; and especially if they had a title to any degree of intimacy with the President. Witness the honors paid to Mr. Martin Folkes when he travell'd into Italy, tho' after Sir Isaac's death. Nor did foreigners when in England value themselves a little if they could pay a visit to Sir Isaac; many of whome, the most considerable men in all parts of the globe, came hither for that very purpose, and thought the hazards of their voyage overpaid in enjoying that privilege.

The second was the honour of knighthood, aptly described this time by Sir David Brewster:

In the month of April 1705, which her Majesty was spending at her royal residence of Newmarket, she went on the 16th. accompanied by Prince George of Denmark, and her whole court to visit the University of Cambridge, where she was to be the guest of Dr. Bentley at Trinity Lodge. "Alighting at the Regent Walk," says Dr. Monk, " before the schools, she was received by the Duke of Somerset, the Chancellor, the head of the University, and addressed in a speech by Dr. Ayloffe, the public orator. From thence her Majesty went in procession to the Regent House, where, agreeably to ancient custom, was held the congregation of the senate, termed *Regia Comitia*, at which the University conferred degrees upon all persons nominated by the Royal Command; the presence of the sovereign dispersing with statutable qualifications and exercises. Afterwards the Queen held a court at Trinity Lodge, where she rendered this day memorable, by conferring knighthood upon the most illustrious of her subjects, Sir Isaac Newton. A sumptuous dinner was then given to the royal visitor and her suite in the Hall of Trinity College, which had been newly fitted up and decorated. Whoever is acquainted with the large sums which *Alma Mater* has since expended on public objects will be surprised to learn, that she was then so poor as to be compelled to borrow £500 for the purpose of this entertainment. The royal party, after attending evening service, at the magnificent chapel at King's College, took leave of the University, and returned the same night to Newmarket."

Newton was about sixty years old when he was honoured by the Sovereign, and by the Royal Society. The presidency of the latter was a fitting tribute to the worth of his scientific achievements, and his knighthood established him as a public figure. Though these two distinctions are inter-related, they reflect the main currents of Newton's professional life. On one hand, there is the man of science, so closely associated with the Royal Society; on the other, the public servant, whether as Member of Parliament, or Master of the Royal Mint. One side of his life had its roots in Cambridge, the other flourished in London.

But seldom does his professional life reveal the whole man, and certainly not in the case of Newton. For example, though his name has always been associated with the law of gravitation, and to a lesser extent with recoinage, it is not generally known that his writings on theology would have produced the equivalent of some seventeen volumes of average size today. A modern authority on Newton, Professor E. N. da C. Andrade, directs attention to the depth of Newton's theological studies and describes his library as rich in books of theological interest, such as the works of the Fathers of the Church—Athanasius, Augustine, Gregory of Nazianzus, Tertullian and many others. Archbishop Tenison is recorded to have said to him, "You know more divinity than all of us put together." The philosopher John Locke wrote: "Mr. Newton is a very valuable man, not only for his wonderful skill in mathematics, but in divinity too, and his great knowledge of the Scriptures, wherein I know few his equals. . . ." Professor Andrade estimates that in the manuscripts on theological matters which Newton left there are some 1,300,000 words.

A striking confirmation of the place that theological studies occupied in Newton's life may be found in a document written more than two hundred years ago. The mathematician John Craig was a friend of Newton and, within eighteen days of the latter's death in 1727, Craig gave an account of the theological manuscripts:

This I know that he [Sir Isaac Newton] was much more solicitous in his inquiries into Religion than into Natural Philosophy. . . . Sir Isaac Newton, to make his inquiries into the Christian religion more successful, had read the ancient writers and ecclesiastical historians with great exactness, and had drawn up in writing great collections out of both and to show how earnest he was in religion, he had written a long explication of remarkable parts of the Old and New Testaments while his understanding was in its greatest perfection lest the infidels might pretend that his applying himself to the study of religion was the effect of dotage. That he would not publish these writings in his own time, because they showed that his thoughts were sometimes different from those which are commonly received, which would engage him in dispute; and this was a thing which he avoided as much as possible. But now it's hoped that the worthy and ingenious Mr. Conduitt will take care that they be published.

To understand the significance of Newton's theological writings it is necessary to appreciate the theological background of the seventeenth century, as well as his own early upbringing. The dominant factor in the religious life of Europe from the sixteenth century was the Reformation. Luther had, in 1520, issued three famous treatises: the first to the laity, urging them to take in hand the reformation of the Church; the second to the theologians, concerning the captivity of the Church; and the third to the Pope, entitled *On the Freedom of a Christian*. The intellectual interests that had been stirred by the Renaissance, with its appeal to classical thought, resulted in the spread of humanism throughout northern Europe. This movement, which began in Italy, laid emphasis on man rather than on the supernatural, and thus broke through the medieval tradition of scholastic theology and philosophy. Humanism has been described as the parent of all modern developments whether intellectual, scientific, or social. In particular, Erasmus realised that the civilising influences of knowledge might be used to combat the evils of the day, and he sought to apply the new learning for the well-being of the common man. If his efforts had been favourably received, the reform of the Roman Church might have taken place from within. It was inevitable that the wider outlook of the Renaissance should have a profound effect on men's attitude to arbitrary authority.

Though the Reformation and its causes are too complex to review briefly, some reference to the objects of the Reformers is desirable in view of Newton's support of their cause. Dr. H. McLachlan, in his book *Isaac Newton; Theological Manuscripts* (1950), writes: " It is certain that Newton's posthumous works were intended to uphold Protestantism and combat the claims of the Roman Church. This zeal is confirmed by his numerous manuscripts on Scripture, Church History and Christian Doctrine."

To continue with the objects of the Reformers, three may be traced which cover, in simple statement, the large field affected. First, it was essential to re-establish church discipline, which had in many directions become lax; secondly, a reform of doctrine was considered long overdue; and thirdly, a lessening of dogmatic control, and an increase in the individual's right of private judgment, based on the Scriptures, were desired. The Protestant Reformation resulted in Counter-Reformation within the Roman Church: its aim was twofold, namely, to reclaim those who had abandoned the Roman faith for the beliefs of Protestantism, and in addition to correct the abuses which had brought about the Reformation. The Society of Jesus, whose members are known as Jesuits, was organised at Paris in 1534 by St. Ignatius of Loyola for the purpose of foreign missions. The wide range of endeavour, which has included such distant fields as French Canada, Mexico, Brazil, Spanish America, India, China and the Philippines, shows the zeal of the Society for missionary work. In the realm of education, Jesuit schools may be regarded as the best in seventeenth century Europe. Jesuits were naturally employed during the Counter-Reformation to combat the arguments put forward on behalf of Protestantism. Mention should also be made of the Inquisition, or the Holy Office, which dates from the twelfth century: this ecclesiastical court became extremely active in searching out Protestant supporters and bringing them to trial.

Such was the background of religious activity in the sixteenth and seventeenth centuries. Added to this were the religious wars and persecutions, such as that of the Huguenots. In the realm of the intellect, too, there appeared an irrepressible urge to break with any position that could only be held on the grounds of authority. The Schoolmen had accepted the Aristotelian tradition into their theology, so that to attack the former was counted as an onslaught on Christianity itself. In 1616 the Qualifiers for the Holy Office maintained that the Copernican theory (namely that the sun was the centre of the universe and immovable), was false and absurd, and formally heretical and contrary to Scripture. Further, that the doctrine that the earth was not the centre of the universe, but moved and has further a daily motion, was philosophically false and absurd and theologically at least erroneous.

Newton's early days were spent in a religious atmosphere—his step-father and an uncle were in Holy Orders. At Grantham the two officiating ministers of the church which he attended were ultimately rejected from their livings for nonconformity. From such men Newton heard Sunday by Sunday their beliefs concerning the Bible, sacerdotalism and ritual. Over the Church porch was an old library given by a Puritan clergyman of a neighbouring parish. Its contents would not only serve mainly to support the preaching of such incumbents as those just described, but also was available for all who could read. It is unlikely that the young Newton, even then an omnivorous reader, would not be influenced by this literature. Little is known of Newton's theological interests at Cambridge; like his contemporaries, he was a master of Latin. All the editions of the Greek Fathers in his library were in both Greek and Latin, but the inference must not be drawn that his knowledge of Greek was slight, for most Greek classics were edited with Latin versions on the opposite page. On the contrary, his Greek has both accents and breathings, and his Hebrew the Massoretic points, so that he seems to have been well equipped to pursue privately his theological studies. In view of the voluminous nature of his writings in this field there is no reason to believe that theology was excluded from the leisure and quiet of those early years at Woolsthorpe, where his first scientific discoveries were made. Indeed this may be regarded as implicit in Craig's expression of opinion already mentioned (p. 156).

The desire, expressed by Craig, that the theological writings should be published is only the beginning of a long sequence of events which delayed publication of even a fraction of the manuscripts for more than two hundred years. The story is told in detail by Dr. McLachlan. Controversy on whether Newton's theological views were too unorthodox for publication played an important part in the delay. Mrs. Catherine Conduitt (Newton's niece, *née* Barton) in the codicil to her last Will and Testament, 26 January, 1737, provided that "my Executor do lay all the tracts relating to Divinity before Dr. Sykes, in hopes he will prepare them for the press. . . . Dr. Sykes to peruse them here [i.e. at her home Cranbury Park, Hampshire]." John Conduitt died in 1737 and his wife in 1739. In 1740 their only child, Catherine, married John Wallop, Viscount Lymington, son of the first Earl of Portsmouth, and thus the Newton manuscripts passed into the possession of the Portsmouth family at Hurstbourne Park, North Hampshire. It was some fifteen years afterwards, probably in 1755, that Dr. Sykes was asked to carry out the provisions of Mrs. Conduitt's will. He was then a sick man and died from paralysis in 1756.

Various writers had seen the Newton manuscripts, but not until 1934 was an adequate survey made by Professor L. T. More, of Cincinnati University. It is fortunate for the interested reader that in 1950 there appeared, as a separate volume, some of Newton's theological manuscripts edited by Dr. H. McLachlan. It should be noted that in 1936 the Newton Papers were offered for sale by order of Viscount Lymington. Lord Keynes ultimately acquired a considerable proportion of these, and in 1946 his Newton collection was bequeathed to King's College, Cambridge.

The subjects included in the Newton manuscripts are varied and include: Chronology, Apocalyptic Literature, Church History, Prophecy, Ecclesiastical Polity, the Nature and Content of Religion, the Relation of Jews and Christians, Roman Catholicism, the Sibylline Oracles, Solomon's Temple, Trinitarianism and New Testament Textual Criticism. To these were added copious extracts from the Bible, patristic literature and early ecclesiastical history. A fairly comprehensive reading list for even the modern theological student!

The following extracts are taken from Dr. McLachlan's edition. In the Preface to the first group of manuscripts headed Irenicum, Dr. McLachlan says: "These writings on Christian Doctrine, Church Government, Relations of Church and State, and the conditions governing membership of the church, though brief, constitute one of the most important of the Newton theological manuscripts. Its purpose is, apparently, to promote comprehension in the established church and set forth a *modus vivendi* for English Protestants."

One of the unfinished drafts consists of nine "positions", the first of which reads:

In the religion of the Jews the two first and great commandments were "Thou shalt love the Lord thy God with all thy heart and with all thy soul and with all thy mind and thou shalt love thy neighbour as thyself. Upon these two commandments hang all the Law and the Prophets." *Matt. XXII, 37.*

Newton then develops the theme with reference to the early history of the Jews and sums up the Christian attitude in the "Third Position".

The loving God and neighbour is also the principal part of the religion of Christians. For this is the love of God that we keep his commandments, and the love of neighbour is that charity without which no man can be saved. *1 John V, 3; 1 Cor. XIII; Rom. XIII, 8-10; Jas. II, 8.* This commandment have we from him that he who loveth God love his brother also. *1 John IV, 21.*

Newton then continues with reference to the primitive Church. The "Sixth Position" is of special interest:

If any man of this religion have been either false Prophets or otherwise wicked; it will not follow from thence that the religion itself is either false or wicked.

A scheme of Old Testament chronology is then developed in which one year is represented by one week leading up to Jesus as the Messiah. This unfinished draft concludes with the "Ninth Position".

In the second Psalm are these words "Thou art my son, this day have I begotten thee. Ask of me and I shall give thee the heathen for thine inheritance and the utmost parts of the earth for thy possession. Thou shalt break them with a rod of iron and shalt dash them in pieces like a potter's vessel." And these words the Apostles and primitive Christians applied to Jesus Christ as being the son of God by the resurrection from the dead, and being to come again in the end of ages, and rule all nations with a rod of iron. *Acts XXIII, 37; Rom. I, 4.*

Another draft of *Irenicum* emphasises Newton's belief in the simplicity of the Gospel and of what is fundamental in Christian belief.

The first principles of the Christian religion are founded, not on disputable conclusions, or human sanctions, opinions, or conjectures, but on the express words of Christ and his Apostles, and we are to hold fact the form of sound words of scripture. . . . The Apostle Paul opposed the preaching of the law of Moses to the Gentiles and called it another gospel whereby the faith in Christ was made void, not because the Law was evil (for the Apostle tells us that the Law is good) but because it was not necessary to salvation, and therefore not to be imposed as a fundamental article of communion. And for the same reason the imposing of any Proposition (true or false) as an Article of Communion, which was not an Article of Communion from the first preaching of the Gospel may be preaching another Gospel; and the persecuting of any true Christians for not receiving that Gospel may be persecuting Christ in his mystical members, and the Persecutor breaks the second and third great commandments in making war upon Christ, and may deserve the name of an Anti-Christian in a literal sense.

A Church guilty of this crime is in a state of apostasy from Christ.

Again, Newton's attitude to the Creeds is expressed thus:

The Constantinopolitan Creed, usually called the Nicene Creed and the Creed usually called the Creed of Athanasius are not therefore any part of the milk for babes in the Church of England, but are to be referred to the strong meats for them that are of ripe age; and therefore to fall out about them proceeds from the want of charity. They are indeed appointed by the Common Prayer Book to be read in the Churches upon certain occasions. And so are many parts of the Scriptures which we do not understand, as *Dan. IX, X; Apoc. IV, VII, XII, 7–13; XIV, 6, 19; 1–17.* We daily dispute about the meaning of these and many other parts of Scripture without falling out about them, and are allowed to do so. And so we may about the meaning of the two Creeds, notwithstanding their being read in Churches.

The Church of England in her 21st Article declared that General Councils (forasmuch as they be an assembly of men whereof all be not governed with the spirit and word of God) may err and sometimes have erred in things pertaining to God: and therefore things ordained by them as necessary to salvation have neither strength nor authority, unless it be declared that they are taken out of the holy Scripture. And in the 8th Article she declares that the three creeds are to be received because they may be proved by most certain warrants of holy Scripture. She doth not require us to receive them by authority of General Councils, and much less by authority of Convocations, but only because they are taken out of the Scriptures. And therefore we are authorised by the Church to compare them with the Scriptures, and see how and in what sense they can be deduced from thence. And when we cannot see the Deduction we are not to rely upon the Authority of Councils and Synods, but may endeavour to learn from others how they may be deduced, and that others are not to fall out with us for doing so.

The draft headed *Irenicum: or Ecclesiastical Polity tending to Peace* consists of twenty theses. Thesis 7 reads: " It is therefore the duty of bishops and presbyters to govern the people according to the laws of God and the laws of the king, and in their councils to punish offenders according to those laws, and to teach those who do not know the laws of God; but not to make new laws in the name of either God or the king." The last sentence of Thesis 12 is also significant: "And the 3,000 baptised by Peter were a Christian church, though they had not yet a bishop, or presbyter, or synagogue, or form of government." Newton's views concerning different churches are expressed in Thesis 17:

To distinguish churches from one another by any difference in customs or ceremonies, or in other laws than the Laws of God, is improper, and tends to superstitions. And if the distinction occasions a breach of communion, the person insisting upon it as a matter of religion is guilty of the schism. For the distinction being taken from things which are only of human authority and external to religion, ought not to be considered as a part of religion, nor to enter into the definition of a Church.

These extracts from *Irenicum* have been made at some length because they reveal Newton's attitude to ecclesiastical authority. The latter was evidently much in his thoughts, which is not surprising in view of the early influences of his life. Indeed, the troubled religious atmosphere of the times was associated with James II's attempt to re-introduce that ecclesiastical authority which had been rejected at the English Reformation.

Another aspect of Newton's theological writings is his interest in Trinitarianism. This subject demands special mention, not only because of its depth and the discussions that have arisen round it, but also for the effect that its study may have had on Newton himself, especially with regard to his decision to remain a layman. It is not always easy to appreciate the bitter controversies concerned with the nature of the Godhead. The term "Trinitarianism" as used above should not, however, be confused with a Roman Catholic religious order of this name, which was founded in 1198 for the ransom of Christians in captivity to the Muhammadans. The doctrine of the Trinity is closely associated historically with the heresy of Arius (256–336) a Presbyter of Alexandria. The Arian position that the Son was created by, and essentially different from, the Father, gave rise to the controversy at the Council of Nicaea, in the year 325. This controversy centred round the Greek word *homoousios* which represented the Orthodox position that the Son was of the same Being as the Father. In opposition to this the Arian position was associated with the Greek word *heteroousios*, implying that the Son was of an essentially different nature from the Father, though pre-existent. In the post-Nicene period the watch-word of the Arian party was the Greek *homoios* meaning "similar", and ultimately there appeared the word *homoiousios* meaning "similar essence". It was the Arian heresy which gave rise to another of Newton's theological writings, namely, *Queries regarding the word "Homoousios"*. This consists of twenty-three queries: the following extracts indicate Newton's attitude and, with the exception of 1 and 2, they suggest an affirmative answer.

Query 1. Whether Christ sent his apostles to preach metaphysics to the unlearned common people, and to their wives and children?

Query 2. Whether the word "homoousios" ever was in any creed before the Nicene; or any creed was produced by any one bishop at the Council of Nice for authorizing the use of that word?

Query 3. Whether the introducing the use of that word is not contrary to the Apostle's rule of holding fast the form of sound words?

Query 4. Whether the use of that word was not pressed upon them by the Emperor Constantine the Great, catechumen not yet baptized and no member of the Council? . . .

Query 11. Whether Athanasius, Hilary, and in general the Greeks and Latins, did not, from the time of the reign of Julian the Apostate acknowledge the Father, Son and Holy Ghost to be three substances, and continue to do so till the Schoolmen changed the signification of the word Hypostasis, and brought in the notion of the three persons in one single substance.

Query 12. Whether the opinion of the equality of the three substances was not first set on foot in the reign of Julian the Apostate, by Athanasius, Hilary, etc.?

The first statements of an unfinished MS. on religion are as follows:

1. That religion and philosophy are to be preserved distinct. We are not to introduce divine revelations into Philosophy nor philosophical opinions into religion.
2. Men are not to be deprived of communion without violating the conditions upon which they were admitted into com munion.
3. That Religion and polity, or the laws of God and the laws of men, are to be kept distinct. We are not to make the commandments of men a part of the laws of God.

The sixth one reads:

6. By communion, I understand a fellowship in the worship of that church, so as to join with them in their public prayers, praises, thanksgivings, and in celebrating the Eucharist; and by excommunication, a deprivation of that communion.

The document entitled *Paradoxical Questions concerning the Morals and Actions of Athanasius and his Followers* is too lengthy for detailed examination, but Dr. McLachlan's Preface to this document adequately describes it:

The Catalogue of Newton Papers reports (p. 73) that of the *Paradoxical Questions* there are "Drafts of various Portions, some in several states, in all about 30,000 words on 120 pp., un-numbered and confused . . . and many sheets imperfect." Brewster (*Memoirs* II, 272) quotes from a copy which he de-scribes in a footnote as "written in Sir Isaac's own hand and extends to sixty-two folio pages. It wants the last leaf." He adds that in the catalogue of Newton's MSS. made in 1777 by Bishop Horsley and his colleague, two copies of this MS. are mentioned in one place and elsewhere another is mentioned as complete, "showing that the other two were not so." The MS. belonging to the King's College Collection, is undoubtedly complete and written by Newton, except a sentence added at the end in pencil by another hand.

The evidence relating to MSS. is important as proving the time and labour given by the writer to this subject. The MS. here copied is beautifully written and amply documented. It was named by Mrs. Conduitt amongst those she desired to be published.

Here is a sustained, closely reasoned attempt to prove, in the words of Lord Keynes, "the dishonesty and falsification of records for which St. Athanasius was responsible", and it is marked by a vein of irony. The result is a portrait of the fourth-century theologian and interpretation of events in which he was the principal actor in strong contrast with those given by historians from the eighteenth century to our own day. It is "Newton" (not Athanasius) "*contra mundum*", though in 1749 Whiston (*Memoirs*, p. 601) described Athanasius "a notorious Forger and Lyar".

In a MS. concerning the language of the Prophets, Newton writes:

He that would understand a book written in a strange language must first learn the language, and if he would understand it well must learn the language perfectly. Such a language was that wherein the Prophets wrote, and the want of sufficient skill in that language is the main reason why they are so little understood. John did not write in one language, Daniel in another, Isaiah in a third and the rest in others peculiar to themselves, but they all write in one and the same mystical language, as well known without doubt to the sons of the Prophets as the Hieroglyphic language of the Egyptians to their priests. And this language, so far as I can find, was as certain and definite in its signification as is the vulgar language of any nation whatsoever, so that it is only through want of skill therein that Interpreters so frequently turn the Prophetic types and phrases to signify whatever their fancies and hypotheses lead them to. He therefore that would understand the old Prophets (as all Divines ought to do) must fix the signification of their types and phrases in the beginning of his studies. . . . The Rule I have followed has been to compare the several mystical places of scripture where the same prophetic phrase or type is used, and to fix such a signification to that phrase as agrees best with all the places: And as critics for understanding the Hebrew consult also other oriental languages of the same root; so I have not feared sometimes to call in to my assistance the Eastern expositors of their mystical writers (I mean, the Chaldee Paraphrast and the Interpreters of Dreams) following herein the example of Mr. Mede and other late writers. For the language of the Prophets, being Hieroglyphical, had affinity with that of the Egyptian priests and Eastern wise men, and therefore was anciently much better understood in the East than it is now in the West. I received also much light in this search by the analogy between the world natural and the world politic. For the mystical language was founded in this analogy and will be best understood by considering its original.

To turn now to Newton's Common Place Book—a folio volume bound in limp vellum with entries in English and Latin—the following paragraph appears:

In Queen Mary's reign, in a little above 5 years' time there were according to the truest account, no fewer than 284 Protestants burnt at the stake for professing the Gospel, besides those that died in prison or were exiled. Nay, the author of the preface to Bishop Ridley's book *De coena Domini*, who is commonly supposed to have been Grindal that was afterwards Archbishop of Canterbury—a person who by his circumstances and troubles in the time of that bloody reign, and by his station and quality under Queen Elizabeth, had as fair advantage as any of being informed concerning the number of those that suffered—tells us there were above eight hundred put to most cruel kinds of death for religion in the two first years of Queen Mary's persecution. *No Protestant Plot*, Part 3d, page 3.

Aeneas Sylvius, who afterwards was Pius II, gave this character to the Popedom, that there was never any great slaughter in Christendom, nor any great calamity happened either of Church or State, whereof the Bishops of Rome were not the Authors. *Hist. Austria.* And as much is said by Machiavelli in his *History of Florence*, Reflections on the Roman Clergy, at the end of the *Politics of France*.

Beneath the surface of these simple statements one may discern that deep-seated sense of justice, that devotion to the spirit of freedom and that personal loyalty to the Protestant cause, so characteristic of Newton the man, and so vividly portrayed from time to time in his theological writings.

Before turning from Newton's theological writings, mention must be made of the Silesian mystic Jacob Boehme (1575–1624). Of him Brewster in his *Memoirs* writes: "The Rev. Mr. Law has stated that there were found among Sir Isaac's papers large extracts out of Jacob Boehme's works, written with his own hand, and that he had learned from undoubted authority that in a former part of his life he was led into a search of the philosopher's tincture from the same author." The reference is to William Law (1686–1761), an Anglican divine and author of *A Serious Call to a Devout and Holy Life*. This book exerted a considerable influence on John Wesley (1703–91) and other leaders of the Methodist evangelical revival. Very considerable controversy has in recent years arisen concerning the passage quoted above, and the possible influence of Boehme on Newton's outlook in philosophy and physics.

It is beyond the scope of this book to marshal the arguments that have been put forward. Perhaps the last word has not yet been written; but at least it can be said that the conflicting views expressed tend to throw into relief some of the many influences which were at work moulding the complex structure of philosophical and scientific thought in the seventeenth century.

It is not of course possible entirely to separate the theological writings of Newton from the general background of his life and thought. The documents mentioned in the preceding chapter dealt with specific matters of religion—Christian experience, church history and biblical interpretation—and as such they throw light on Newton's contention that "religion and philosophy are to be preserved distinct" (see page 166). But this must not be thought to suggest that among his many interests there was no room for philosophy in its broadest sense. Indeed he may be regarded as the mature advocate of certain philosophical arguments, put forward by his predecessors and contemporaries, to support a belief in the existence of God. It is therefore desirable to assess the contemporary philosophical atmosphere—whether at the University of Cambridge, in London or on the Continent.

In any survey of the general philosophical background of the seventeenth century, one name is outstanding, namely, that of René Descartes. The well-known dictum *"cogito ergo sum"* —"I think, therefore I exist"—not only influenced philosophical thought for some two hundred years, but also it may be regarded as a culmination of an attitude towards life and the universe which had been gaining ground since the Renaissance. The attitude may be described as anthropocentric. This emphasis on man and his achievements can be discerned in the expansion of Europe from the restrictions of medieval life. It is evident in the exploration and discoveries which resulted in the spread of European culture to the new World, as well as in the establishment of trade routes towards the East. It may also be seen in the political and territorial aspirations of the European powers and in the colonial wars associated with their realisation. In art, architecture, music and literature, man reached unexpected heights, and the invention of movable type enabled him to spread abroad his thoughts and achievements. Francis Bacon and René Descartes created an atmosphere which has dominated the modern world; and in the realm of natural philosophy, new theories concerning the universe kindled the hope that man's intellect would always be sufficient to penetrate the mysteries of Nature.

With such a background it is easy to see how the works of man tended to overshadow the claims of revealed religion, and thereby point the way to an age of reason and enlightenment. Yet one of the characteristics of many scientists in the seventeenth century was the conviction that their discoveries did actually support a belief in the existence of God. This theme has recently been discussed (1958) in one of the Yale Historical Publications (*Science and Religion in Seventeenth-Century England* by Richard S. Westfall). The author stresses the importance of Boyle's work *The Christian Virtuoso* and describes the attitude of other " virtuosi ", or scientists, the final chapter being devoted to Newton. These two men, Boyle and Newton, hold a unique position as they both desired to bring the theme of the existence of God to the notice of all thoughtful people. Boyle's paralytic stroke in 1670 did not prevent his continued interest in this and a variety of subjects, or his correspondence with notable men abroad. By the year 1691 he was very ill, and in preparing his will, he arranged for an income of £50 a year to establish an annual salary for a learned divine, or preaching minister of London, to deliver eight sermons in a parish church of the city " for proving the Christian religion against notorious Infidels, *viz.* Atheists, Theists, Pagans, Jews, and Mahometans, not descending lower to any controversies, that are among Christians themselves ". So were founded the well-known Boyle Lectures. The first sermon was preached in 1692 by Richard Bentley, later Master of Trinity College, Cambridge, in St. Martin's Church, London, where Boyle was buried. Bentley's theme was " A Confutation of Atheism ", and in the last sermon of the series he developed an argument for a Divine Providence based on the nature of the universe as revealed in the *Principia*. Before these sermons were printed, Bentley submitted the manuscripts to Newton for criticism.

In a recently published work entitled *Isaac Newton's Papers and Letters on Natural Philosophy*, Professor Bernard Cohen of Harvard has edited a comprehensive collection of Newton's writings. The Introduction to section IV—" Newton's Four Letters to Bentley, and the Boyle Lectures related to Them "—

has been written by Perry Miller, who points out that "the principal source of the atheism Bentley had to counteract was Thomas Hobbes" (1588–1679) and although the latter's position had been attacked from the philosophical and ethical standpoints, "it seemed to the guardians of Christianity that the tide of atheism had not been checked; clearly a new method was required". To this Bentley devoted himself and sought the help and support of Newton. The correspondence cannot be quoted here, but Newton's opening sentence in a letter to Bentley, dated December 10, 1692, is revealing: "When I wrote my Treatise about our System, I had an Eye upon such Principles as might work with considering Men, for the Belief of a Deity, and nothing can rejoice me more than to find it useful for that Purpose." The four letters of Newton were preserved by Bentley and were published after his death. The title page reads *Four Letters from Sir Isaac Newton to Doctor Bentley containing some Arguments in Proof of a Deity* and the year of publication is 1756. One of the interesting features of Professor Cohen's book is the facsimile reproduction of these letters and indeed of many other of the Newton documents.

At the beginning of the third book of the *Principia* entitled "The System of the World", Newton writes:

In the preceding Books I have laid down the principles of philosophy; principles not philosophical but mathematical: such, namely, as we may build our reasonings upon in philosophical inquiries. These principles are the laws and conditions of certain motions, and powers or forces, which chiefly have respect to philosophy; but, lest they should have appeared of themselves dry and barren, I have illustrated them here and there with some philosophical scholiums, giving an account of such things as are of more General Nature, and which philosophy seems to be founded on; such as the density and the resistance of bodies, spaces void of all bodies, and the motion of light and sounds. It remains that, from the same principles I now demonstrate the frame of the System of the World. Upon this subject I had, indeed, composed the third Book in a popular method, that it might be read by many; but afterwards, considering that such as had not sufficiently entered into the principles could not easily discern the strength of the consequences, nor lay aside the prejudices to which they had been many years accustomed, therefore, to prevent the disputes which might be raised on such accounts, I chose to reduce the substance of this Book into the form of Propositions (in the mathematical way), which should be read by those only who had first made themselves masters of the principles established in the preceding Books: not that I would advise anyone to the previous study of every Proposition of those Books; for they abound with such as might cost too much time, even to readers of good mathematical learning. It is enough if one carefully reads the Definitions, the Laws of Motion, and the first three sections of the first Book. He may then pass on to this Book, and consult such of the remaining Propositions of the first two Books, as the references in this, and his occasion shall require.

Then follow " Rules of Reasoning in Philosophy ", and comments on them. The rules are:

I. We are to admit no more causes of natural things than such as are both true and sufficient to explain their appearances.
II. Therefore to the same natural effects we must, as far as possible, assign the same causes.
III. The qualities of bodies, which admit neither intensification nor remission of degrees, and which are found to belong to all bodies within the reach of our experiments, are to be esteemed the universal qualities of all bodies whatsoever.
IV. In experimental philosophy we are to look upon propositions inferred by general induction from the phenomena as accurately or very nearly true, notwithstanding any contrary hypothesis that may be imagined, till such time as other phenomena occur, by which they may either be made more accurate, or liable to exceptions.

The third Book of the *Principia* deals with the application of the law of universal gravitation to the problems of the solar system, including that of the tides on the earth. Newton follows his custom throughout the whole work of introducing at various points certain *scholia*. The term was originally used with reference to an annotation on a passage in a Greek or Latin author. Newton's use of the word is that of an explanatory note or comment on some aspect of previous work. A more lengthy *General Scholium* follows Proposition XXXI of Book II, which gives some account of Newton's pendulum experiments in a resisting medium. The words *General Scholium* are mostly used when referring to the final scholium mentioned in the next paragraph.

The first edition of the *Principia* ended with a discussion of the paths of comets, but in the second edition this was followed by the *General Scholium*. It might be thought that Newton added this summary as a statement of his philosophical attitude to science, and as a confession of faith in the main purpose of natural philosophy, which he believed was to inspire character and promote religion. There is, however, another factor to which due weight must be given, namely, the attack made by Continental mathematicians, between the dates of publication of the first and second editions of the *Principia*, on Newton's philosophy.

It is fortunate that letters have been preserved of correspondence between Newton, Bentley and Cotes on this subject: the letters concerned have been grouped together by J. Eddleston, a Fellow of Trinity College, Cambridge, in a book published in 1850 with the descriptive title: *Correspondence of Sir Isaac Newton and Professor Cotes, including Letters of Other Famous Men, now first published from the Originals in the Library of Trinity College, Cambridge.* Opposite the title-page is an engraving of Newton, and underneath are his signature, and written in his own handwriting, *hypotheses non fingo.* This phrase has usually been translated "I do not frame hypotheses": it will be seen later (page 178) that "frame" may not fully interpret the meaning of *fingo* in late Latin.

The letters just mentioned show that the attack by Continental mathematicians on the *Principia* was the result of the controversy with Leibniz over priority of discovery of the calculus, and that it was directed against the hypothetical character of the Newtonian philosophy. Newton had claimed that his philosophy did not involve hypothesis, whereas that of Descartes involved the assumption of vortices. This gives colour to the opening sentence of the *General Scholium*: "The hypothesis of vortices is pressed with many difficulties."

As Bentley and Cotes were both entrusted with the preparation of the second edition of the *Principia*—Bentley on the financial and business side and Cotes on the actual revision—they were much concerned at this latest attack from the supporters of Leibniz. Descartes was held in high esteem, and his views dominated the philosophical outlook of the seventeenth century. His theory of vortices was based on a hypothesis of vortices in an occult medium; the word "occult" is applied to a substance which cannot be directly perceived by the senses. Newton held that his position did not involve any such hypothesis; he maintained that attraction at a distance was an essential property of matter. His opponents argued that by so doing he had introduced an occult quantity and that his philosophy was as hypothetical as the Cartesian hypothesis of vortices in an occult medium.

The *General Scholium* in its opening paragraph explains how the theory of vortices is untenable. Newton also maintains that no merely mechanical causes could give birth to so many regular motions; they presuppose the existence of a Divine Creator. He discusses the attributes of the one Supreme God and concludes this part of the argument: "And thus much concerning God: to discourse of whom from the appearance of things, does certainly belong to Natural Philosophy." Newton ends the *General Scholium* with his refutation of the charge that he had introduced an occult quantity and made hypotheses in putting forward the idea of gravitational attraction at a distance:

But hitherto I have not been able to discover the cause of those properties of gravity from phenomena, and I frame no hypotheses; for whatever is not deduced from the phenomena is to be called an hypothesis; and hypotheses whether metaphysical or physical, whether of occult qualities or mechanical, have no place in experimental philosophy. In this philosophy particular propositions are inferred from the phenomena, and afterwards

M

rendered general by induction. Thus it was that the impenetrability, the mobility, and the impulsive force of bodies, and the laws of motion and of gravitation, were discovered. And to us it is enough that gravity does really exist, and act according to the laws which we have explained, and abundantly serves to account for all the motions of the celestial bodies, and of our sea.

And now we might add something concerning a certain most subtle spirit which pervades and lies hid in all gross bodies; by the force and action of which spirit particles of bodies attract one another at near distances, and cohere, if contiguous; and electric bodies operate to greater distances, as well as attracting the neighbouring corpuscles; and light is emitted, reflected, refracted, inflected, and heats bodies; and all sensation is excited, and the members of animal bodies move at the command of the will, namely, by the vibrations of this spirit, mutually propagated along the solid filaments of the nerves, from the outward organs of sense to the brain and from the brain into the muscles. But these are things that cannot be explained in few words, nor are we furnished with that sufficiency of experiments which is required to an accurate determination and demonstration of the laws by which this electric and elastic spirit operates.

Newton's use of the word hypothesis has given rise to much controversy. It is fair to say that the meaning of the word must be viewed in its general context, so that it is not surprising that Newton does not always use the word in the same sense. The phrase *"hypotheses non fingo"* first appears in the second edition of the *Principia* (1713), in the *General Scholium* to Book Three. One of the factors that should be taken into account is the translation of the Latin *fingo*. In later Latin *fingo* could be translated " I imitate ", or, in the language of the stage, " I act a part ". In any event, Newton is contrasting such hypothetical consideration with his own deductions based on observation and experiment.

It is obviously not possible to follow here in any detail the points which arise from Newton's writings on philosophical and metaphysical matters. Attention should however be directed to an interesting study by Professor I. Bernard Cohen, of Harvard University, published in 1956, under the title, *Franklin and Newton: An Inquiry into Speculative Newtonian Experimental Science and Franklin's Work in Electricity as an Example Thereof.* The two main sources of the Newtonian philosophy are the *Principia* and *Opticks*, and the difference in treatment was aptly described by Clerk Maxwell in 1876: "Newton, in his *Principia*, deduces from the observed motions of the heavenly bodies the fact that they attract one another according to a definite law. . . . In his *Principia*, he confined himself to the demonstration and development of this great step in the science of the mutual actions of bodies. He says nothing about the means by which bodies are made to gravitate towards each other. We know that his mind did not rest at this point— that he felt that gravitation itself must be capable of being explained, and that he even suggested an explanation depending on the action of an ethereal medium pervading space. But with that wise moderation which is characteristic of his investigation he distinguished such speculations from what he had established by observation and demonstration, and excluded from his *Principia* all mention of the cause of gravitation, reserving his thoughts on this subject for the 'Queries' printed at the end of the *Opticks*." Thus the "Queries" provide the key to Newton's philosophy and indicate the width and depth of his thought.

There is one aspect of Newton's genius that should now be considered and which has sometimes been overlooked. To quote again from Professor Bernard Cohen's book (*Franklin and Newton*): "Though much has been written about Newton and Newtonians, most of the literature in the recent past has tended towards a static, rather than dynamic, point of view. General works on intellectual history, and even books on the growth of science or of physics in particular, have concentrated on Newton's positive achievements, rather than on the guide posts he set for the advancement of experimental science. In such books we learn of the invention of the calculus, the analysis of white light and of colour, and the principles of dynamics. For the most part, however, we do not find much about Newton's speculations and hypotheses concerning subtle elastic fluids, the nature and structure of matter, or the inter-action between matter and radiation—all of which were the source of inspiration for the heroic creations of the speculative experiments of the eighteenth century." Not the least valuable of Professor Cohen's book on Franklin and Newton is the evidence he adduces in support of this claim. Indeed the ability to erect sign-posts for the guidance of future generations is one of the marks of true greatness in any branch of human achievement.

It is perhaps worth while emphasising one aspect of Newton's natural philosophy which has specially influenced the course of science, including the biological sciences. It may be summed up in the word simplicity—not using this word to suggest that the *Principia* is easy to comprehend. The simplicity of Newton's law of universal gravitation, compared with the Ptolemaic system, consists in the formulation of one law for all celestial and terrestrial bodies. A. D. Ritchie has recently (1958) directed attention to a special feature of the two systems, namely, their contrast in simplicity. The following extract is taken from *Studies in the History and Methods of the Sciences:*

True, the geocentric theory could not be maintained in its original and most attractive form as suggested by Eudoxus, in terms of simple concentric spheres. The geocentric theory did have to be a bit complicated, but the heliocentric theory held no great hopes of really drastic simplification. So Ptolemy argued, with the backing of the great Hipparchus. Nobody could possibly have anticipated the drastic simplification introduced by Kepler and Newton, whereby one set of laws suffices for all heavenly bodies (and terrestrial too) instead of a separate one for each planet. That came of abandoning circular orbits for elliptical ones. Had any Greek mathematician the technique which Kepler had for calculating orbits? The circle is not only the " perfect " figure; far more important, it is the only figure of uniform curvature with which calculation is relatively easy. Multiplication of cycles and epicycles did not make calculation impossible and could cope with the evidence pretty well. Its only disadvantage was that each cycle and epicycle was a new *ad hoc* hypothesis, and the whole Ptolemaic "system" was not a single system at all. It was a hotch-potch which did not solve Plato's problem—to produce *a* geometrical construction. It took Kepler and Newton together to solve that problem.

The simplicity just described led to far-reaching results, and in unexpected studies. Professor Charles Singer in *A Short History of Medicine*, 1944, claims that the constant pursuit of the man of science " since the days of Newton, has been the pursuit of Law, and he has always been satisfied that Law has only to be sought in order to be found. This conception has affected the medical and biological sciences very deeply. Thus the influence of the Newtonian philosophy is as traceable in them as it is in the astronomical and physical sciences. Galileo showed men of science that weighing and measuring are worth while. Newton convinced a large proportion of them that weighing and measuring are the *only* investigations that are worth while. . . . The eighteenth century dawned with the refreshing breeze of Newtonian philosophy blowing through it. During the previous two hundred years there had been an immense amount of new and fruitful research along diverse lines. Chemistry and Mechanics, Botany and Comparative Anatomy, Descriptive Anatomy and Experimental Physiology, Epidemiology and Microscopic Analysis, all had yielded startling results. The new generation was bewildered with the very mass and novelty of the material. The Biologists of the time must have been well nigh hopeless of reducing their vast accumulations to order, when they contemplated the beauty and symmetry of the mathematical relations that Newton and his followers had introduced into Cosmic conceptions. Thus the eighteenth century is a period for Biology of pause and consolidation during which attempts were made to introduce unitary conceptions into the mass of accumulated material."

In spite of his philosophical and other interests Newton's enthusiasm for practical matters led him to carry out a large number of experiments in the related spheres of alchemy or chemistry. There is a letter to Francis Aston, his friend and contemporary at Cambridge, which reveals how diverse were the subjects in which Newton was interested. This letter is of value too as being one of the few personal ones which has been preserved. Aston became secretary of the Royal Society in 1678 but resigned in 1686; he generously bequeathed an estate in Lincolnshire to the Society, and personal property worth £445. At the time of the letter, Aston, a year older than Newton, was about to make a tour of the Continent. Because of the variety of its contents the letter is quoted in full:

Trinity College, Cambridge.
18 May, 1669.

SIR,

Since in your letter you give mee so much liberty of spending my judgment about what may be to your advantage in travelling, I shall do it more freely than perhaps otherwise would have been decent. First, then, I will lay down some general rules, most of which, I believe, you have considered already; but if any of them be new to you, they may excuse the rest; if none at all, yet is my punishment more in writing than yours in reading. When you come into any fresh company, (1) Observe their humours. (2) Suit your own carriage thereto, by which insinuation you will make their converse more free and open. (3) Let your discours be more in queries and doubtings than peremptory assertions or disputings, it being the design of travellers to learne, not to teach. Besides, it will persuade your acquaintance that you have the greater esteem of them, and soe make them more ready to communicate what they know to you; whereas nothing sooner occasions disrespect and quarrels than peremptorinesse. You will find little or no advantage in seeming wiser, or much more ignorant than your company. (4) Seldom discommend any thing though never so bad, or doe it but moderately, lest you bee unexpectedly forced to an unhandsome retraction. It is safer to commend any thing more than it deserves, than to discommend a thing soe much as it deserves; for commendations meet not soe often with oppositions, or, at least, are not usually soe ill resented by men that think otherwise, as discommendations; and you will insinuate into men's favour by nothing sooner than seeming to approve and commend what they like; but beware of doing it by a comparison. (5) If you be affronted, it is better, in a forraine country,

182

to pass it by in silence, and with a jest, though with some dishonour, than to endeavour revenge; for, in the first case, your credits ne'er the worse when you return into England, or come into other company that have not heard of the quarrell. But, in the second case you may beare the marks of the quarrell while you live, if you outlive it at all. But, if you find yourself unavoidably engaged, 'tis best, I think, if you can command your passion and language, to keep them pretty eavenly at some certain moderate pitch, not much hightning them to exasperate your adversary, or provoke his friends, nor letting them grow over much dejected to make him insult. In a word, if you can keep reason above passion, that and watchfulness will be your best defendants. To which purpose you may consider, that, though such excuses as this,—He provok't mee so much I could not forbear,—may pass among friends, yet amongst strangers they are insignificant, and only argue a traveller's weaknesse.

To these I may add some general heads for inquirys or observations, such as at present I can think on. As, (1) To observe the policys, wealth, and state affairs of nations, so far as a solitary traveller may conveniently doe. (2) Their impositions upon all sorts of people, trades, or commodities, that are remarkable. (3) Their laws and customs, how far they differ from ours. (4) Their trades and arts, wherein they excell or come short of us in England. (5) Such fortifications as you shall meet with, their fashion, strength, and advantages for defence, and other such military affairs as are considerable. (6) The power and respect belonging to their degrees of nobility or magistracy. (7) It will not be time mispent to make a catalogue of the names and excellencys of those men that are most wise, learned, or esteemed in any nation. (8) Observe mechanicisms and manner of guiding ships. (9) Observe the products of nature in several places, especially in mines, with the circumstances of mining and of extracting metals or minerals out of their care, and of refining them; and if you meet with any transmutations out of their own species into another, (as out of iron into copper, out of any metall into quicksilver, out of one salt into another, or into an insipid body etc.) those, above all, will be worth your noting, being the most luciferous, and many time lucriferous experiments too in philosophy. [The two words "luciferous" and "lucriferous" are used in alchemy to distinguish experiments which advanced knowledge from those which added income.] (10) The prices of diet and other things. (11) And the staple commiditys of places.

These generals (such as at present I could think of) if they will serve for nothing else, yet they may assist you in drawing up a modell to regulate your travels by.

As for particulars, these that follow are all that I can now think of, viz. Whether at Schemnitium, in Hungary (where there are mines of gold, copper, iron, vitriol, antimony, etc.), they change iron into copper by dissolving it into a vitriolate water, which they find in cavities of rocks in the mines, and then melting the slimy solution in a strong fire, which in the cooling proves copper. The like is said to be done in other places, which I cannot now remember; perhaps, too, it may be done in Italy. For about twenty or thirty years agone there was a certain vitrioll came from thence (called Roman vitrioll) but of a nobler virtue than that which is now called by that name; which vitrioll is not now to be gotten, because, perhaps, they make a greater gain by some such trick as turning iron into copper with it, than by selling it. (2) Whether in Hungary, Sclavonia, Bohemia, near the town Eila, or at the mountains of Bohemia near Silesia, there be rivers whose waters are impregnated with gold; perhaps, the gold being dissolved by some corrosive waters like *aqua regis*, and the solution carried along with the streams, that runs through the mines. And whether the practise of laying mercury in the rivers, till it be tinged with gold, and then straining the mercury through leather, that the gold may stay behind, be a secret yet or openly practised. (3) There is newly contrived, in Holland, a mill to grind glasses plane withall, and I think polishing them too; perhaps it will be worth the while to see it. (4) There is in Holland one—Berry, who some years since was imprisoned by the Pope, to have extorted from him secrets (as I am told) of great worth, both as to medicine and profit, but he escaped into Holland, where they have granted him a guard. I think he usually goes cloathed in green. Pray inquire what you can of him, and whether his ingenuity be any profit to the Dutch. You may inform yourself whether the Dutch have any trick to keep their ships from being all worm-eaten in their voyages to the Indies. Whether pendulum clocks do any service in finding out the longitude, etc.

I am very weary, and shall not stay to part with a long compliment, only I wish you a good journey, and God be with you.

Is. Newton.

Pray let us hear from you in your travels. I have given your two books to Dr. Arrowsmith.

It may be that the modern reader of this letter may also feel "very weary"; its references however to transmutations and in particular, knowledge for its own sake as distinct from knowledge for gain (luciferous and lucriferous), are typical of alchemy. Of interest also is the reference to the mountains of Bohemia with its silver mines at Joachimsthal—it was from these mines that silver coins were produced in the sixteenth century, and from the termination of the name they were known as "thalers" for short, from which ultimately came the name "dollar". Further, from these mines, at the end of the nineteenth century, the Austrian Government provided a ton of the mineral pitchblende (which contains uranium) for the early researches of M. Curie. It will be agreed that whatever interpretation is put on the letter as a whole, and there have been expressed differences of opinion, the diversity of topics mentioned is an indication of the variety of interests in Newton's life.

A detailed account of Newton's studies in alchemy and chemistry is beyond the scope of this book, but the following extracts indicate something of his interest in such matters. John Collins, a man whose scientific knowledge had been attained by his own efforts, made a casual remark about his friend Newton, in a letter to Gregory in the year 1675. "Mr. Newton, I have not writ to or seen these eleven or twelve months, not troubling him as being intent upon chemical studies and practices, and both he and Dr. Barrow beginning to think mathematical speculations to grow at least dry, if not somewhat barren." There is also the well-known description of the laboratory in Newton's room at Trinity College, Cambridge, near the east end of the Chapel. This was given by Dr. Humphrey Newton in response to Conduitt's request for material for a life of Newton.

About 6 weeks at spring, and at 6 at the fall, the fire in the elaboratory scarcely went out, which was well furnished with chymical materials as bodyes, receivers, heads, crucibles, etc., which was made very little use of, the crucibles excepted, in which he fused his metals; he would sometimes, tho' very seldom, look into an old mouldy book which lay in his elaboratory, I think it was titled *Agricola de Metallis,* the transmuting of metals being his chief design, for which purpose antimony was a great ingredient.

The book referred to would be Agricola's *De re metallica* published in 1556. Georg Agricola (the Latinised form of the name Bauer) was a German scholar (1490-1555): he has been referred to as "the father of mineralogy", and the book is a systematic treatise on mining and metallurgy. Humphrey Newton of Grantham served Newton from 1683 to 1689 as his assistant and amanuensis and so could write of such matters with authority, especially as his association covers the period of the preparation and publication of the *Principia*.

Newton's references to chemical matters, in his letter to Aston, have been interpreted by L. T. More as evidence that Newton was "a credulous alchemist". It is however difficult to associate such credulity with a mind capable of wresting from Nature the secrets of gravitation. Fortunately Professor Douglas McKie, referring to More's statement writes (*Philosophical Magazine*, p. 849, 1942), "A recent biographer of Newton concluded from this letter [i.e. the letter to Francis Aston] that its writer was 'a credulous alchemist', commented on his naïve inquiries 'about the processes of changing iron into copper', and added that these inquiries 'give us a glimpse of his youthful ambition to devote himself to luciferous experiments, and of his dreams of turning such knowledge into the lucriferous creation of gold', while 'it was with great reluctance and after long years of labour that he finally became sceptical of the pretensions of alchemy'. For this verdict, there seems to be no evidence at all, as we shall presently show. As for the alleged conversion of iron into copper, it had only recently been shown by Van Helmont that, contrary to the generally accepted opinion, the copper was already in the solution and was merely precipitated by the iron, an explanation that Newton accepted later on."

Professor McKie also directs attention to two statements of H. Newton (the second is quoted above, page 184). In the first he (Humphrey Newton) admits that he did not know the aim of Newton's experiments; in the second, he claims that his master's chief design was the transmuting of metals. Such apparently contradictory statements do not inspire confidence, and the reference to Agricola, who disliked alchemists, does not support the view that Newton was an alchemist. Further, antimony had long been in use for alloys, and from 1672 Newton had experimented with it in order to discover a suitable alloy for use as a mirror in a reflecting telescope.

From Aston's letter and from what is known of Newton's own apparatus, it may be safely assumed that the latter was interested in chemical experiments in much the same way as were his contemporaries. Professor McKie successively investigates in detail the various sources which reveal Newton's attitude towards this branch of science. For example, in a letter to Boyle, February 1679, Newton showed that the supposition of " an aethereal medium " could be applied to explain certain chemical phenomena, but with caution he writes in the first paragraph of the letter:

The Truth is, my notions about things of this kind are so indigested, that I am not well satisfied myself in them; and what I am not satisfied in, I can scarce esteem fit to be communicated to others; especially in natural philosophy, where there is no end of fancying.

Newton, as well as Boyle, was influenced by the well-known Netherlands chemist Johan Baptist van Helmont (1577 or 1580–1644). The latter had revived the theory, associated historically with Thales of Miletus in the sixth century B.C., that water was the source of all substances, except air. The following passage from the *Principia* should be read with this in mind:

The vapours which arise from the sun, the fixed stars, and the tails of the comets, may meet at last with, and fall into, the atmospheres of the planets by their gravity, and there be condensed and turned into water and humid spirits; and from thence, by a slow heat, pass gradually into the form of salts, and sulphurs, and tinctures, and mud, and clay, and sand, and stones, and coral, and other terrestrial substances.

Special reference must be made to Newton's only chemical paper—*De natura acidorum.* John Harris had Newton's permission to publish this paper, which was probably written about 1692. It appeared in 1710 with the following introduction in the supplementary volume of John Harris' *Lexicon Technicum* (London 1704). Copies of this volume are now extremely rare.

The following Paper of Sir Isaac Newton's is excellently well worth the Philosophical Reader's most serious and repeated Perusal; for it contains in it the Reason of the Ways and Manner of all Chymical Operations, and indeed of almost all the Physical Qualities, by which Natural Bodies, by their small Particles, act upon one another. . . . But however, to do the Illustrious Author yet further Justice, I have, with his Leave, at the end of this *Introduction* Printed a *Latin* Paper of his *De Acido*, with a Translation of my own: and which, tho' never Publish'd before, was given by him to a Friend, as long since as the Year 1692. . . .

The paper has as its main theme the attractive force between the particles of acids and those of other substances—a subject developed more fully in the "Queries" appended to the *Opticks*. With regard to these Queries, an ample account is given in Professor McKie's article in the *Philosophical Magazine* for 1942 "Some Notes on Newton's Chemical Philosophy written upon the Occasion of the Tercentenary of his Birth'.

The following extract from the last Query number 31, summarises Newton's views concerning the small particles of bodies to which he refers at the beginning of the Query.

All these things being consider'd, it seems probable to me, that God in the Beginning form'd Matter in solid, massy, hard, impenetrable, moveable Particles, of such Sizes and Figures, and with such other Properties, and in such Proportion to Space, as most conduced to the End for which he form'd them; and that these primitive Particles being Solids, are incomparably harder than any porous Bodies compounded of them; even so very hard, as never to wear or break in pieces; no ordinary Power being able to divide what God himself made one in the first Creation. While the Particles continue entire, they may compose Bodies of one and the same Nature and Texture in all Ages: But should they wear away or break in pieces, the Nature of Things depending on them, would be changed. Water and Earth, composed of old worn Particles and Fragments of Particles, would not be the same Nature and Texture now, with Water and Earth composed of entire Particles in the Beginning. And therefore, that Nature may be lasting, the Changes of corporeal Things are to be placed only in the various Separations and new Associations and Motions of these permanent Particles; compound Bodies being apt to break, not in the midst of solid Particles, but where those Particles are laid together and only touch in a few points.

It seems to me farther, that these Particles have not only a *Vis inertiæ*, accompanied with such passive laws of Motion as naturally result from that Force, but also that they are moved by certain active Principles, such as is that of Gravity, and that which causes Fermentation and the Cohesion of Bodies. These Principles I consider not as occult Qualities, supposed to result from the specifick Forms of Things, but as general Laws of Nature, by which the Things themselves are form'd; their Truth appearing to us by Phenomena, though their Causes be not yet discover'd. For these are manifest Qualities, and their Causes only are occult.

No account of Newton's writings would be complete without some reference to his laborious researches into chronology. Modern archaeology has so progressed recently as to alter the conception held, even a few years ago, of the early history and chronology of mankind. The science of geology too has thrown much light on the cultures of early man and the vast periods of pre-history, in addition to the countless preceding ages during which life was evolving on the planet. To understand the atmosphere in which Newton lived, all such results of modern scholarship must be laid aside. There were two accepted dates in human chronology, namely, the year 4004 B.C. as the date of the Creation and 2348 B.C. as that of the Flood. The first was introduced into the Church of England by James Ussher (1581–1656), Archbishop of Armagh in Northern Ireland, and subsequently used in later editions of the Authorised Version of the Bible, also known as King James Version of the Bible. Both dates depend on the general chronology of the Old Testament, and of course on the division of the years into those reckoned before the birth of Christ (B.C.) and those which came after (A.D.). This division of time into B.C. and A.D. was worked out by a Christian scholar of the sixth century, one Dionysius Exiguus (the word may refer to his small stature, or his humility), who was abbot of a monastery in Rome.

Such was the general background accepted by Newton in *The Chronology of Ancient Kingdoms* and his object is outlined with characteristic humility in the introduction: " I have drawn up the following chronological table, so as to make chronology suit with the course of nature, with astronomy, with sacred history, with Herodotus the Father of History, and with itself; without the many repugnancies complained of by Plutarch. I do not pretend to be exact to a year: there may be errors of five or ten years, and sometimes twenty, and not much above." From the modern reader's standpoint the details of this chronology have but little value. There is however much human interest in the way that Newton originally set pen to paper. Caroline of Ansbach, the daughter of a Hohenzollern margrave of Ansbach, not far from Nuremberg in Germany, married in 1705 the electoral prince of Hanover, who subsequently ascended the throne of Great Britain in 1727 as George II. When the latter's father became king in 1714 as

George I, Caroline naturally took the title of Princess of Wales, as her husband had assumed that of Prince of Wales. Caroline's interest in philosophy, associated with her sojourn in Hanover, led her to introduce regular meetings of philosophers in London. Newton was among the guests who attended these weekly discussions and the Princess asked his advice concerning the education of her children. This led Newton to describe a system of chronology which he had evolved while at Cambridge, and he promised to prepare a manuscript for private use, entitled: *A Short Chronicle from the First Memory of Things in Europe to the Conquest of Persia by Alexander the Great*. It was this copy, loaned to the Abbé Conti on the understanding that it would not be made public, that led to the subsequent appearance of Newton's work on the subject. Under the title, *The Chronology of Ancient Kingdoms Amended*, it was published in 1728, a year after Newton's death. This volume of 376 quarto pages represented some three years of concentration when Newton was over eighty-one and suffering from ill-health. The Abbé Conti's breach of faith regarding the contents of Newton's manuscript, had led to its publication on the Continent without the author's consent. The somewhat complicated story has been told in detail by Professor C. T. More in his book *Isaac Newton*.

Some of the many interests of Newton's long life have now been mentioned. The mere cataloguing of these does not bring out the elusive quality of personality. Yet the breadth of interest, strong personality and outstanding achievements in natural philosophy, which blazed the trail for future generations of scientists—all these were combined in the stately figure who was hailed doyen of British Science by visitors from abroad and who, as his closing years approached, was held in increasing affection and esteem by his countrymen.

The choice of title for this chapter is not intended to suggest a specific landmark or date in Newton's life, which would serve as a dividing line between the main current of his manhood and his closing years. For some men such a division is not only possible but even inevitable. The break which comes with retirement, especially when life has been concentrated on work to the exclusion of other interests, may involve a complete and perhaps shortlived change.

In the life of Newton, however, there is no such boundary. His numerous and varied interests do not admit division of his life into watertight compartments. It is characteristic that the two offices of President of the Royal Society, and Master of the Mint, both of which reveal his breadth of outlook, were held continuously by Newton for a period approaching thirty years, until his death in 1727 at the age of eighty-four.

In the arena of public life there appears, from time to time, a dignified and worthy figure, " the elder statesman ", a leader, whose advancing years and wealth of experience fit him for a role apart, acknowledged by all. The generation of his contemporaries is diminishing, younger men in increasing numbers are shouldering the old responsibilities and facing new problems. The elder statesman remains, an integral part of the changing scene, able and willing to give advice, encouragement and continuity. The background of the elder statesman is appropriate also to Newton's closing years. There are no abrupt changes; maturity ripens imperceptibly, experience deepens without ostentation, and humility is a garment that becomes life's eventide. The following picture, again drawn from Stukeley's *Memoirs,* provides interesting comment on the day-to-day affairs of the Royal Society, under the guiding hand of its distinguished president:

He himself was a person of a great deal of modesty, in every respect, and always turn'd a deaf ear to any sort of praises of his just merit. Whilst he presided in the Royal Society, he executed that office with singular prudence, with a grace and dignity— conscious of what was due to so noble an Institution—what was expected from his character. When any paper was read, or experiment exhibited, wherein he had any knowledg, and it was very rarely otherwise, he never faild to speak to it, with a just commendation; or to point out its defects, where it might be improv'd, where any experiment might be better directed. He would give a concise history of the advances of the subject, very much to its illustration, and to the emolument of the members present.

I remember particularly that time I officiated for Dr. Halley, a paper was read of the pernicious effects of rooms fresh plaister'd o'er with lime, before dry. Sir Isaac told us of a terrible catastrophe of that sort, of his own knowledg. A man, his wife, and servant-maid—they all lay in one room, when he was a lad at Grantham, which had been newly drawn with fresh lime, and to dry it the sooner they made a fire, and shut the doors, to prevent them catching cold as they thought. In the morning they were every one found in the cold arms of death. After I went to live at Grantham I often heard speak of this tragedy: it happened in a house in West-gate.

Sir Isaac was very careful of giving any sort of discoragement to all attempts of improvement in natural knowledg. There were no whispering, talking, nor loud laughter. If discussions arose in any sort, he said they tended to find out truth, but ought not to arise to any personality. The *Transactions* were publish'd by the Secretarys, with proper care and judgment, and were accordingly esteem'd. He was very solicitous of keeping up a correspondence, both at home and abroad: and that letters should be answer'd, offers of exchange of literary news cultivated, and every thing done that tended to order, the honor and advancement of the Society and the harmony of the members. He said, correspondence was the life of these Societys. He never grudged paying any necessary charge, or that might be expedient. He gave money largely, to assist deserving persons, and where it was wanted.

In addition to his keen interest in the activities of the Royal Society, Newton's own residence became a centre of attraction. In 1708 he had moved from Jermyn Street, London, to Chelsea, then a village on the river Thames some three miles to the west. In 1710 Newton returned to London and, according to the ratebooks of the parish of Westminster, lived at 35, St. Martin's

Street, holding the tenancy until his death in 1727, although he removed to Kensington in 1725 for health reasons. Leicester House, which gives its name to the present Square, was built in the fourth decade of the seventeenth century, and the description Leicester Fields was then appropriate. A street plan of 1682 shows that the area had by then been laid out, including names such as Whitcomb Street and Panton Street which have survived to the present time. There was however no St. Martin's Street until about 1692–93; in the latter year the name first appeared with seven houses in a ratebook. The street was built on *Blue Mews*. The word "mews" originally referred to the buildings which housed hawks, where they were "mewed" in cages; mewing had special reference to the moulting period and is derived from the Latin *mutare*, to change. The nearby royal stables at Charing Cross were built on the site where the royal hawks were formerly "mewed"; so the name "mews" had thus been introduced for stables.

The first tenant at 35, St. Martin's Street, according to the ratebook, was in residence by 1694, so that the house was comparatively new when Newton occupied it in 1710. Subsequently he added a special room as an observatory. On the land next to the house stood the Orange Street Huguenot Chapel, opened in 1693, to serve the increasing number of refugees arriving in London following the Revocation of the Edict of Nantes by Louis XIV. The original edict had been promulgated by Henry IV in 1598 to free his Protestant subjects from persecution and certain disabilities, and to recognise some hundreds of Reformed Churches then existing in France. Newton's Protestant sympathies would be deeply stirred by the injustice of Louis XIV's revocation of the edict, and the presence of the nearby Orange Street Chapel. A picture has been drawn of distinguished people who from time to time could be seen in the congregation. Newton and his niece Catherine Barton are included, as well as de Moivre (1667–1754), the now well-known mathematician whom Newton had befriended when he came to England as a penniless and friendless refugee.

At the house itself, Newton entertained on a large scale and his numerous friends were not limited to those of specially scientific bent. St. Martin's Street was in a fashionable neighbourhood and Newton's home became a centre of the intellectual life of London. All, however, did not appreciate his genius. It is said that when he came to St. Martin's Street he was greeted with a certain amount of suspicion by a widow who was his next-door neighbour. The following description is attributed to her:

He [Newton] diverts himself in the oddest ways imaginable. Every morning when the sun shines so brightly that we are obliged to draw the window-blinds, he takes his seat in front of a tub of soap-suds, and occupies himself for hours blowing soap-bubbles through a common clay-pipe, and intently watching them till they burst.

Newton lived the life of a bachelor, and depended on his niece Catherine Barton to look after him. This she did efficiently despite the following story. Stukeley was invited to dine with Newton, and, after waiting an hour, he decided to have dinner alone and apparently consumed the whole meal. Newton, entering from his study, said, " Give me but leave to take my short dinner, and I shall be at your service. I am fatigued and faint." Then, noticing that only the remains of a meal were left, he said to Stukeley: " See what we studious people are! I forgot that I had dined."

One of the successors of Newton at 35, St. Martin's Street was Dr. Charles Burney, who lived there during 1774-89. Of their advent his daughter, Fanny Burney, writes:

We came ten days ago to this house which we purpose calling "Newton House " or " The Observatory " or something that sounds grand, as Sir Isaac Newton's identical observatory is still subsisting, and we show it to all our visitors as our principal lyon. I am very pleased with the mansion . . . his observatory is my favourite sitting place, where I can retire to read or write my private fancies or vagaries.

Perhaps Fanny, later Madame D'Arblay, was unconsciously influenced by the atmosphere of Newton's house and the adjoining Huguenot Chapel; at any rate she revealed the true spirit

197

of sympathy in her devotion to a later group of French refugees.

By 1913 Newton's house had been scheduled for demolition, and the bricks were found to be unfit for use elsewhere. On the site there now stands the Westminster Central Reference Library. Thus Lord Macaulay's prophecy that the home of Sir Isaac Newton would be well known as long as Britain retains any trace of civilisation has not been fulfilled—at any rate not literally. But through the generosity of Mrs. Babson, an even wider interpretation may be given to Macaulay's words. In the library of the Babson Institute, Massachusetts, is a faithful, full-sized reconstruction of the parlour at 35, St. Martin's Street, with the original woodwork from the house itself. The Grace K. Babson Collection of Sir Isaac Newton contains some of the books written by Newton, including the three editions of the *Principia* and the editions of the *Opticks,* books from his library and various manuscripts. In 1954 a grafted scion of the original Newton apple tree at Woolsthorpe was planted on the campus of the Babson Institute, near the Library.

Mention may here be made of Newton's notebooks. Six of the seven known to exist are now at the University of Cambridge, England; the seventh, the earliest, is in the Pierpont Morgan Library, New York. Thus there have grown up in the United States of America various associations with Newton's life, work and interests. At Babson Park in particular, the original fabric from his house in St. Martin's Street will always be a reminder of the friendship of the English-speaking peoples and of their indebtedness to one of Britain's greatest sons.

In the corners of the garden in the present Leicester Square there are four white marble busts on granite pedestals—Hogarth the artist, Hunter the anatomist, Reynolds the painter; and Newton. All were resident at some time in the immediate vicinity.

Mention has already been made of Newton's part in the controversies with Leibniz, Hooke and Flamsteed. The atmosphere of suspicion and rivalry which prevailed amongst those who were discovering Nature's secrets in the seventeenth and early eighteenth centuries, affected all four men. In addition, personal animosities, faults of temper, and sometimes illness contributed to the bitterness of feeling engendered. But a sense of balance must be preserved, as Professor C. D. Broad pointed out in a lecture at the British Academy in 1927, the two-hundredth anniversary of Newton's death. "The accounts which it has been necessary to give of Newton's quarrels with Hooke, Flamsteed, and Leibniz would produce a highly distorted impression of his character if they were not qualified by reference to special extenuating circumstances and balanced by some account of his many acts of kindness to other scientists."

In this connection there are four younger men whose names must receive more than a passing notice. Roger Cotes, Henry Pemberton, Colin Maclaurin and James Stirling were all mathematicians, and privileged, in one way or another, to be associated with Newton during the later years of his scientific work.

Roger Cotes (1682–1716), son of the Rector of Burbage, Leicestershire, was educated at St. Paul's School, London, making equal progress in both mathematics and classics. Entering Trinity College, Cambridge, at the age of seventeen, he became a Fellow in 1705. In 1707 he was appointed the first Plumian Professor of Astronomy and Experimental Philosophy in the University of Cambridge. The foundation of this chair is of interest, not only because of Cotes' association with Newton, but also as an indication of the change in emphasis that was beginning to be apparent in the studies of the University. In 1704, Dr. Plume, Archdeacon of Rochester, left sufficient funds to found the Plumian Professorship of Astronomy and Experimental Philosophy: Newton served with Flamsteed on a committee to draw up the necessary statutes. Bentley supported the candidature of Cotes; Flamsteed opposed this choice, having already expressed support for John Witty, who was the assistant of William Whiston, then the Lucasian Professor of Mathematics. Flamsteed's feelings were expressed in a letter:

Dr. Bentley has determined, without even so much as letting me know that he was about such business, and, I fear, directly contrary to the archdeacon's design: wherewith, I am apt to think, none of the trustees in Cambridge were so well acquainted as I am. I had not known of it but by an accident. I have wrote about it to Mr. Whiston, who tells me the thing is done as to the nomination of a Professor, and past remedy. I am sorry for it, because this first election will be a precedent for the future, and I fear a very ill one.

Another problem in personal relations! And Flamsteed entered in his diary on 15 March:

Met Dr. Bentley at Garraway's [Coffee House]: Sir I. Newton was there: we discoursed first about Dr. Plume's Astronomical Professorship; the Doctor would have had my hand to a paper for the election of Mr. Cotes to be Professor: I refused till I saw him: he told me Mr. Whiston and Mr. Cotes should wait on me next week.

In 1713 Cotes took Holy Orders, and in the same year began the preparation of the second edition of the *Principia*, at the request, it will be remembered, of Dr. Bentley, who as Master of Trinity College had gathered round him a small group of able and enthusiastic young men to carry forward certain reforms. Bentley soon appreciated Cotes' calibre, but the latter died in 1716 at the early age of thirty-four. Cotes' friendship with Newton was marked by the high esteem in which the older man held the young and promising professor. On receiving news of his premature death, Newton made the memorable observation: " If Mr. Cotes had lived we might have known something."

Henry Pemberton's introduction to Newton was in marked contrast to that of Cotes. Pemberton (1694–1771), was London born and at the age of twenty left England to study medicine at Leyden. Here he came under the influence of Boerhaave (1668–1738), who has been described as the foremost physician of the eighteenth century and who was well known also for the breadth of his scientific interests. While at Leyden, Pemberton had a copy of the *Principia* lent to him and was surprised that he did not find it too difficult to understand. Interest aroused, he continued with Newton's work on fluxions and the *De Quad-*

ratura. From Leyden he went to Paris for the study of anatomy, but his real interests seem to have been elsewhere and, attending a sale, he bought a number of valuable mathematical works. After a short stay in London he returned to Leyden as the guest of Boerhaave and obtained his M.D. in 1719.

Pemberton was attached to St. Thomas' Hospital, London, but did not give much attention to the practice of medicine. His first contact with Newton came through Keill, a mathematician at Oxford, who wrote extolling Pemberton's solution of a mathematical problem propounded by Leibniz. Newton was not very impressed by the young doctor, but the atmosphere changed when Pemberton demonstrated the inefficiency of an attempted proof by the Italian mathematician, Poleni, of Liebniz's assertion that the force of descending bodies was proportional to the square of their velocities. This piece of work, transmitted by Dr. Mead, Newton's physician, so pleased Newton that he ultimately asked Pemberton to edit the proposed third edition of the *Principia*. In contrast with Bentley's treatment of Cotes, the generosity of Newton to Pemberton has already been mentioned. In the preface to his book: *View of Sir Isaac Newton's Philosophy*, 1728, Pemberton pays this tribute:

Though his memory was much decayed, I found he perfectly understood his own writings, contrary to what I had frequently heard in discourse from many persons. This opinion of theirs might arise perhaps from his not being always ready at speaking on these subjects, when it might be expected he should. . . . As to the moral endowments of his mind, they were as much to be admired as his other talents. But this is a field I leave others to expatiate in. I only touch upon what I experienced myself during the few years I was happy in his friendship. But this I immediately discovered in him, which at once both surprised and charmed me: Neither his extreme great age nor his universal reputation had rendered him stiff in opinion or in any degree elated. Of this I had occasion to have almost daily experience. The remarks I continually sent him by letters on his *Principia* were received with the utmost goodness. These were so far from being any ways displeasing to him, that on the contrary it occasioned him to speak many kind things of me to my friends, and to honour me with a public testimony of his good opinion.

Colin Maclaurin (1698–1746) provides another illustration of Newton's capacity for adapting himself to the particular needs of young and promising mathematicians. Maclaurin, probably the most brilliant of Scottish mathematicians, was orphaned by the loss of his father six weeks after birth and of his mother when he was ten years old. At the University of Glasgow his thesis on the power of gravity gained for him his M.A. degree at the age of fifteen. At nineteen, after a competitive examination lasting ten days, Maclaurin was appointed Professor of Mathematics in Marischal College, Aberdeen. In the vacation of 1719 he visited London and met Newton at the Royal Society. Two years later on another visit to London a close friendship was established with Martin Folkes, a Fellow of the Royal Society. Nor were Maclaurin's activities confined to England and Scotland. In 1722 he toured Lorraine and in 1724 he was awarded a prize by the Académie Royale des Sciences in Paris.

Maclaurin was an ardent Newtonian and one of the first to teach the method of fluxions and mechanics. He was elected a Fellow of the Royal Society in 1719. His friendship with Newton he described as the greatest honour and happiness of his life, and it was not long before this friendship resulted in a generous gesture by the older man. When Maclaurin was twenty-seven years old he offered himself to the Curators of the University of Edinburgh as assistant, and later successor, to James Gregory, whose advancing age and infirmity made help essential. Another candidate—a good mathematician and with considerable backing for the part—made Maclaurin's chances slender. In addition, there was no fund available for the post of assistant. Newton wrote the following letter to Maclaurin and gave him permission to show it to the University Authorities:

I am very glad to hear that you have a prospect of being joined to Mr. James Gregory in the professorship of the mathematics at Edinburgh, not only because you are my friend but principally because of your abilities, you being acquainted as well with the new improvement of mathematics, as with the former state of those sciences: I heartily wish you good success, and shall be very glad of hearing of your being elected: I am, with all sincerity, your faithful friend and most humble servant.

As Maclaurin had scruples in making public a private letter, Newton wrote to the Lord Provost of Edinburgh. Receiving an acknowledgment, he wrote again as follows:

I received the honour of your letter, and am glad to understand that Mr. Maclaurin is in good repute amongst you for his skill in mathematics, for I think he deserves it very well. And, to satisfy you that I do not flatter him, and also to encourage him to accept of the place of assisting Mr. Gregory, in order to succeed him, I am ready (if you please to give me leave) to contribute twenty pounds per annum towards a provision for him, till Mr. Gregory's place became void, if I live so long, and I will pay it to his order in London. When your letter arrived at London, I was absent from hence, which made it the later before I received it, otherwise I might have returned an answer a little sooner.

Maclaurin was elected as a result of Newton's influence, and for some twenty years the University must have had frequent cause to be thankful that Newton's advice was followed. Then occurred the tragic circumstance of Maclaurin's death. During the Jacobite uprising of 1745, he helped to remedy the lack of defence precautions at Edinburgh, by actively supervising the plans he himself had made. This involved fatigue and cold to which he was unaccustomed; the effects contributed to his death in 1746 while dictating the last chapter of his commentary on the *Principia*. On the south wall of Greyfriars Church, Edinburgh, is a tablet to his memory with the unique tribute to his genius *Newtono Suadente*—"recommended by Newton".

James Stirling (1692–1770), known as "the Venetian", came into Newton's life with a very different background from that of the three mathematicians already mentioned. Stirling's ancestry largely accounts for the somewhat turbulent nature of his early years. In contrast to Maclaurin, Stirling was involved in the

Jacobite plot of 1715, at any rate by implication, and supported it. His father, Archibald Stirling of Garden, in Stirlingshire, Scotland, the place of James Stirling's birth, and his grandfather, Sir Archibald Stirling of Keir (about five miles from Dunblane, Perthshire), were both Jacobites. At the age of eighteen Stirling was, through influence, nominated an exhibitioner at Balliol College, Oxford. In 1715, at the time of the "First Pretender" to the throne—Prince James, son of the exiled James II—Stirling was expelled from Oxford on account of his correspondence with members of the Keir and Garden families. From Oxford he fled to Venice and taught mathematics. Among the papers he produced was a commentary on Newton's work on curves of the third degree. In appreciation of this, Newton sent Stirling a gift of money and arranged that his work should be published in England. While at Venice, Stirling made the acquaintance of the mathematician Nicola Bernoulli (1687–1759), brother of John Bernoulli (see page 73). By the year 1725 it was known among the glass-makers of Venice that Stirling had discovered one of their trade secrets. The jealousy and spirit of revenge that were stirred up led to Stirling's fear of assassination and consequent desire to leave Venice for England. In this he was helped by Newton, who also obtained a pardon for him. His appreciation of Newton's kindness is expressed in the following extract of a letter to his benefactor:

As your generosity is infinitely above my merit, so I reckon myself ever bound to serve you to the utmost; and indeed a present from a person of such worth is more valued by me than ten times the value from another.

Stirling's work in pure mathematics is well known and, although outside the period of Newton's life, it is of general interest that the applied aspect of science earned him a debt of gratitude from his countrymen. Apart from being a manager of a mine at Leadhills, the accounts of the city of Glasgow for 1752 show that the very first item of expenditure in a ten-million sterling scheme to make Glasgow a seaport, was £28 4s. 4d. for a silver tea-kettle to be presented to " James Stirling, mathematician, for his service, pains, and trouble in surveying the river towards deepening it by locks".

Newton's generosity, however, was not limited to helping younger men. Nor indeed was his help confined to individuals, for the Royal Society benefited from his liberality, particularly towards the end of his life.

But, from the more academic atmosphere of scientific studies, attention must be turned to the closing years of Newton's activities at the Mint. The normal routine and responsibilities of the Master of the Mint during Newton's closing years provide few incidents of note, though his advice of course was increasingly valuable in view of his experience of over a quarter of a century. One incident may however be mentioned as an illustration of Newton's continued mental alertness. In 1720 an inventor, John Rotherham, offered a method of making coins more durable, of defeating men who depreciated bullion with acid, and preventing all counterfeiting, thereby claiming that " the lives of many persons in time to come will be saved ". Further, the new process would save the Government up to £20,000 a year and swell the salaries of the Mint's officers. The only reward that Rotherham asked was a post at the Mint at £1,000 a year for himself and his heirs for ever. When Newton was not interested, Rotherham put his scheme before the Lord Justices and in response to their request Newton advised: "he offers nothing to be examined and without examination I am in the dark and know not what report to make. I take him to be a trifler, more fit to embroil the coinage than to amend it." A year later, having duly elaborated the process with still further prospects of financial gain, Rotherham laid his project before the Privy Council. This led Newton, then an octogenarian, armed with a catechism of twelve questions, to see the inventor. The matter did not rest there, as six years later the mentally unbalanced Rotherham petitioned the King to make the Mint buy his secret!

The story is based on Newton's papers and is quoted by Sir John Craig, Deputy Master and Comptroller of the Mint, and ex-officio Engraver of the King's Seals, 1938-47. It is fortunate that in his book *Newton at the Mint* he had access to these

Newton MSS. Craig's assessment, as an economist, of Newton's work at the Mint is therefore of considerable value. He describes the enduring changes which Newton made in the Mint as:

First, coins were required to be struck at their individual right weights; the principle of complete conformity with standard of fineness being on the contrary rejected, though a step was taken towards it; and secondly a legal officer was introduced for legal work.

There is however, in addition to the technical skill and administrative ability which Newton brought to the Mint, one quality—that of integrity—which was of inestimable value at a time when corruption in high places was common. In 1724 Newton was consulted on the question of clemency to a counterfeiter convicted at Derby Assizes, but he advised against it:

'Tis better to let him suffer, than to venture his going on to counterfeit the coin and teach others to do so until he can be convicted again, for these people very seldom leave off. And 'tis difficult to detect them.

From the age of eighty Newton's vigour was declining. In 1722 he showed signs of serious illness—an affection of the bladder—and was advised by his physician, Dr. Mead, to take life more leisurely and avoid much travel. To ease the burden of Royal Society affairs, Martin Folkes was appointed Deputy President. At the Mint, Newton's resignation was avoided, it is said, by the proffer of Conduitt's help. Newton's health improved sufficiently for him to undertake some of his accustomed tasks, and it will be remembered that Pemberton kept in close touch with him over the preparation of the third edition of the *Principia*.

In August 1724, however, Newton's illness was diagnosed as stone in the bladder, and in the following January he suffered from congestion of the lungs, and later from gout. The air of Leicester Square in London was not considered good for his health, so he moved to what was then the " village " of Kensington, about two miles to the west. Stukeley describes a visit to Newton, then in his eighty-fourth year:

On 15 April, 1726, I paid a visit to Sir Isaac at his lodgings in Orbels buildings in Kensington, dined with him and spent the whole day with him alone. . . . After dinner, the weather being warm, we went into the garden and drank thea, under the shade of some apple trees, only he and myself. Amidst other discourse, he told me, he was just in the same situation, as when formerly, the notion of gravitation came into his mind. It was occasion'd by the fall of an apple, as he sat in a contemplative mood. Why should that apple always descend perpendicularly to the ground, thought he to himself. Why should it not go sideways or up-wards, but constantly to the earth's centre? Assuredly, the reason is, that the earth draws it. There must be a drawing power in matter: and the sum of the drawing power in the matter of the earth must be in the earth's center, not in any side of the earth. Therefore dos this apple fall perpendicularly, or towards the center. If matter thus draws matter, it must be in proportion of its quantity. Therefore the apple draws the earth, as well as the earth draws the apple. That there is a power, like that we here call gravity, which extends its self thro' the universe.

Newton's house was in Pitt Street and was only demolished in 1894. It stood on the rising ground to the north of Kensington Church and west of Church Street. This is a very different area now from the secluded countryside of over two hundred years ago where Stukeley listened to Newton's reminiscences of his greatest scientific discovery. It is a homely picture—the aged philosopher sipping tea with his friend after dinner in the shade of trees the fruit of which will always be linked with the discovery of the law of gravitation.

Though Newton had been persuaded to move to Kensington, his heart was still in London, which through the years had be-come so closely bound up with his own life. Conduitt says, ". . . though he found the greatest benefit from rest, and the air at Kensington, and was always the worse for leaving it, no methods that were used could keep him from coming sometimes to town"—a longing that the true Londoner can appreciate.

Newton felt well enough to travel to London on 28 February, 1727, and he presided over the meeting of the Royal Society on Thursday, 2 March; but on his return to Kensington on 4 March, he was seriously ill, suffering great pain. Though some improvement could be discerned by the middle of the month, and Newton was able to read and talk to Dr. Mead in the morning of Saturday, 18 March, he lapsed into unconsciousness in the evening, and died in the early morning of 20 March, 1727.

So closed a long life of outstanding scientific achievement and public service. Newton's body lay in state in the Jerusalem Chamber of Westminster Abbey, and he was buried within the Abbey itself. His funeral was a national tribute to his greatness, and the monument to his memory, erected over his tomb in 1731, portrays the many interests of his life. The following is a translation of the Latin inscription:

HERE LIES

SIR ISAAC NEWTON, KNIGHT,

Who, by a vigour of mind almost supernatural,

First demonstrated

The motions and Figures of the Planets,

The Paths of the Comets, and the Tides of the Ocean.

He diligently investigated

The different refrangibilities of the Rays of Light

And the properties of the Colours to which they give rise.

An Assiduous, Sagacious, and Faithful Interpreter

Of Nature, Antiquity, and the Holy Scriptures,

He asserted in his Philosophy the Majesty of God,

And exhibited in his Conduct the simplicity of the Gospel.

Let Mortals rejoice

That there has existed such and so great

AN ORNAMENT OF THE HUMAN RACE

Born 25th Dec. 1642, Died 20th March 1727.

It is characteristic of the truly great man that he stands out alone from the contemporary scene; through him the heritage of the past is enriched and the course for the future set. Though he may, in a sense, be regarded as the product of the age in which he lived, he can never be identified with it or merged into the general background of his time. By these standards Newton's position is assured among men of science. "If I have seen further, it is by standing on the sholders of giants," he wrote to Hooke in 1676. But it is not only the more distant vision gained thereby that was characteristic of Newton: he also transformed previous discoveries and isolated theories into a coherent whole. Constant reference has been made to his generalisations. Herein is the enrichment of heritage that is one of the marks of true greatness. For here, the special case gives place to the more general one; the particular to the universal, the limits of terrestrial motion and earth's attraction, to the unbounded realms of celestial mechanics, in whose domain the same laws of motion hold, and where the local force of gravity is included in the wider conception of universal gravitation.

With equal vision Newton set the course of study for generations to come, and his resting place in Westminster Abbey has been made symbolic of his influence on the future of science. Surrounding and almost adjoining the stone slab which marks his grave are smaller ones, bearing the names of Faraday, Clerk Maxwell, Lord Kelvin, J. J. Thomson and Lord Rutherford. These were some of the "giants" who followed in his steps. Little could they or he have realised where the course that he had set would lead, what vistas would be revealed, and the almost limitless resources which would be made available for man's welfare.

Up to the nineteenth century it had indeed seemed that the Newtonian mechanics with its independent time and three-dimensional space would endure as the permanent framework within which to study the Universe. Then there emerged another great figure—Albert Einstein (1879–1955). He gave new colour to the world of mathematical physics which he had inherited, and reached forward into uncharted realms of related

o

space and time, in which the Newtonian system itself becomes a special case of the more comprehensive theory of relativity. But without the Newtonian system there could not have been a theory of relativity.

So Newton remains alone—unique among his contemporaries, and of all time, the greatest of the men of science. His varied interests and his "queries" concerning ultimate realities give added meaning to his own estimate of his life.

I do not know what I may appear to the world; but to myself I seem to have been only a boy playing on the sea-shore, and diverting myself in now and then finding a smoother pebble or a prettier shell than ordinary, whilst the great ocean of truth lay all undiscovered before me.

In the ante-chapel of Trinity College, Cambridge, are memorial statues to some of the illustrious sons of the College. On one side, Francis Bacon and Dr. Isaac Barrow; on the opposite side, Dr. Whewell, Lord Tennyson and Lord Macaulay. At their head, alone, facing the eastern end of the Chapel, Sir Isaac Newton with the simple inscription:

NEWTON

Qui genus humanum ingenis superavit

Who surpassed all men of genius

1 MS ON GRAVITY [*facing page* 65]

A paper of Newton on gravitation, probably written between 1667 and 1671. On 3rd October, 1953, the *Manchester Guardian* published an article by Professor H. W. Turnbull, F.R.S., entitled " Isaac Newton's Letters " in which reference was made to the document, a part of which is reproduced in this illustration.

The original consists of a single folded sheet with no title; it was discovered by Professor Turnbull before 1953, when preparing Volume I of Newton's Correspondence. The significance of the paper is discussed at length by Dr. A. R. Hall in the *Annals of Science*, Volume XIII, March 1957. There are also notes on this document in *Isaac Newton's Correspondence*, Volume I, edited by H. W. Turnbull, 1959; Professor Turnbull's translation is given below.

The calculations contained in this document, especially those which imply that the centripetal accelerations of planets are inversely proportional to the squares of their distances from the sun, may indicate that at the time of writing Newton was already in possession of the idea of universal gravitation and the inverse square law.

Translation

1 When a body A is rotating in a circle AD towards D, its endeavour from the centre is just as much as would in the time AD (which I take to be very minute) carry it off to a distance DB, since it would cover that distance in that time if only it were to move freely along the tangent AB without hindrance to its endeavour.

Now, since this endeavour, provided that it act continually in a straight line as in the case of gravity, impels bodies through spaces which are as the squares of the times; in order to know through how much space they impel them in the time of one revolution $ADEA$, I seek a line which is to BD as the square of the circumference is to AD^2. Now $BE:BA::BA:BD$ (by Book III of Euclid's *Elements*). And, since between BE and DE, as also between BA and DA, the difference is supposed to be infinitely small, I substitute for them in turn and get $DE:$

$DA :: DA : DB$. Lastly, by making DA^2 (or $DE . DB$) : $ADEA^2$:: $DB : ADEA^2/DE$, I obtain the line sought (namely the third proportional in the ratio of the circumference to the diameter) through which its endeavour of recess from the centre, if constantly applied in the same straight line, would propel a body in the time of one revolution.

For example, since that third proportional is equal to 19·7392 semidiameters; if its endeavour of approach to the centre in virtue of gravity were as much, at the equator, as is its endeavour of recess from the centre due to the daily motion of the Earth; then in a periodic day it would drive a heavy body through $19\frac{3}{4}$ terrestrial semidiameters, or through 69087 miles; and in an hour through 120 miles; and in a minute through $\frac{1}{30}$ mile or $\frac{100}{3}$ paces, that is $\frac{500}{3}$ feet; and in a second through $\frac{5}{108}$ feet, or through $\frac{5}{9}$ inch.

But in fact the force of gravity is great enough to drive heavy bodies downwards about 16 feet in 1 second, that is, about 350 times farther in the same time than the endeavour from the centre; and indeed the force of gravity is so many times greater than what would prevent the rotation of the Earth from causing bodies to leave it and fly up into the air.

2 Corollary. Hence in different circles the endeavours from the centres are as the diameters applied to the squares of the times of revolution, or as the diameters multiplied by [the squares of] the number of revolutions made in any the same time.

So, since the Moon revolves in 27 days, 7 hours and 43 minutes, or in 27·3216 days (whose square is $746\frac{1}{2}$), and is distant 59 or 60 terrestrial semidiameters from the Earth, I multiply the lunar distance 60 by the square of the lunar revolution 1; and 1, the distance of the Earth's surface from the centre, by $746\frac{1}{2}$, the square of the revolutions; and so I have the proportion 60 to $746\frac{1}{2}$, which is that between the endeavour of the Moon and that of the terrestrial surface, of receding from the centre of the Earth. And so the endeavour of the terrestrial surface at the equator is about $12\frac{1}{2}$ times greater than the endeavour of the Moon to recede from the centre of the Earth. And so the force of gravity is 4000 and more times greater than the endeavour of the Moon to recede from the centre of the Earth. And if that endeavour from the Earth causes her always to turn the same face towards the Earth, the endeavour of this lunar-terrestrial system to recede from the Sun should be less than the Moon's endeavour of recess from the Earth, otherwise the Moon would face the Sun rather than the Earth.

But in order to make a more accurate estimate of this matter I suppose 100000 to be the distance of the lunar system from the Sun, and y the distance of the Moon from the Earth. And since the Moon completes 13 revolutions 4 signs 12 degrees 52 minutes in a sidereal year, or 13·369 revolutions (whose square is 178·73); I multiply 100000, the distance of the Sun, by unity, the square of its revolution, and y the distance of the Moon by 178·73, the square of its revolution, and get [the ratio] 100000 to 178·73y as the force of the Earth from the Sun to the force of the Moon from the Earth. Whence it is established that the distance of the Moon from the Earth ought to be greater than $\dfrac{100000}{178\cdot73}$, or 559$\frac{1}{2}$, with respect to the distance 100000 of the Sun. And thence the greatest solar parallax in the lunar orbit will not be less than 19 minutes, and the Sun's horizontal parallax at the Earth not less than 19 seconds, reckoned when the Sun and Moon are distant 90 degrees from their apogees. But take the parallax to be 24 seconds, and then the lunar distance from the Earth will be 706$\frac{3}{4}$, and the ratio of its endeavour of recess from the Earth to the Earth's endeavour of recess from the Sun will be about 5 to 4; and indeed the force of gravity will be 5000 times greater than the endeavour of recess of the Earth from the Sun. Let 100000 be the semidiameter of the great orb and x that of the Earth, and 365$\frac{1}{4}$ × 365$\frac{1}{4}$ x (or 132408) will be [to unity] as the endeavour of a man away from the Earth to his endeavour away from the Sun.

Finally, among the primary planets, since the cubes of their distances from the Sun are reciprocally as the squared numbers of their periods in a given time, their endeavours of recess from the Sun will be reciprocally as the squares of their distances from the Sun: for example in Mercury, Venus, Earth, Mars, Jupiter, Saturn as $\frac{4}{27}$, $\frac{10}{19}$, 1, 2$\frac{5}{16}$, 27$\frac{1}{8}$, 90$\frac{5}{6}$; or as 1, 3$\frac{5}{9}$, 6$\frac{3}{4}$, 15$\frac{2}{3}$, 183$\frac{1}{2}$, 614$\frac{1}{2}$ reciprocally; Or directly as 614; 173; 91; 39; 3$\frac{1}{3}$, 1.

3 A rotating pendulum and a pendulum swinging to-and-fro return in the same time, if they hang to the same depth.

4 If a rotating pendulum and a pendulum swinging to-and-fro hang to the same depth, the arc of the swing, described from the perpendicular, is proportional to the chord of [twice] the arc which the rotating pendulum describes in the same time.

2 LETTER TO HALLEY [*facing page* 128]
This letter to Halley is of particular interest, being written by Newton in his eighty-third year, after he had moved to Kensington on the grounds of health. In addition to the characteristic attention to detail which it reveals, two references in it may be specially noted, the first being the parabolic orbit of the comet of 1680: the second Newton's mention of the second edition of the *Principia* ("my principles").

3 REFLECTING TELESCOPE [*facing page* 129]
Newton's first reflecting telescope was made in 1668 and the second, shown in this illustration, in 1671. In this illustration the eye-piece and mirror are shown separately. The alloy used for the mirror consisted of six parts of copper and two of tin (this alloy was well known to alchemists for its brightness) together with one of arsenic, which Newton believed would enable the surface to take a better polish. Details of his method of polishing are given in the *Opticks*.

Newton had turned his attention to the reflecting telescope because he did not believe that chromatic aberration could be eliminated from the object-glass of a refracting one. The following incident however shows an unexpected interest in the latter type. An object-glass of seven and a half inches aperture and one hundred and twenty-three feet focal length was presented to the Royal Society in 1692 by Constantine Huygens, the brother of Christian. A refracting telescope of such proportions presented special problems of erection, which the Society was prepared to solve by mounting it on a high building for the purpose of zenith observations. Hooke and Halley were instructed to investigate the possibility of using the scaffolding of St. Paul's, as a temporary measure. In 1710 however James Pound erected the telescope at Wanstead Park, near Epping Forest, about 9 miles N.E. of London. For this purpose a maypole was used, which through Newton's influence had been removed from the Strand, London! The pole subsequently bore the humorous inscription:

Once I adorned the Strand,
But now have found
My way to pound
In Baron Newton's land.

Early Books about Newton

STUKELEY, WILLIAM: *Memoirs of Sir Isaac Newton's Life*, London, 1936. Contains the author's reminiscences of his friend.

EDDLESTON, J.: *Correspondence of Sir Isaac Newton and Professor Cotes including letters of other Eminent Men, now first published from the Originals in the Library of Trinity College, Cambridge.* London, 1850. Other unpublished letters and papers by Newton are included, together with a chronological outline of Newton's life.

BREWSTER, SIR DAVID: *Memoirs of the Life, Writings and Discoveries of Sir Isaac Newton.* Two volumes. London, 1855.

BALL, W. W. ROUSE: *An Essay on Newton's Principia.* London, 1893.

Books Associated with Newton Anniversaries

During the twentieth century certain Newton commemorations were the occasion for special books and articles. Some of these are mentioned below.

[a] THE 200TH ANNIVERSARY OF NEWTON'S DEATH 1927:

BROAD, C. D.: *Sir Isaac Newton.* Annual lecture on a master mind. Henriette Hertz Trust of the British Academy. Oxford, 1927.

BRODETSKY, S.: *Sir Isaac Newton,* London, 1927.

GREENSTREET, W. J.: editor, *Isaac Newton, 1642–1727:* a series of articles prepared under the auspices of the London Mathematical Society, London, 1927.

MORE, L. T.: *Isaac Newton,* New York, 1934. Though published later than 1927, this authoritative and comprehensive biography was inspired by the fact that at the bicentenary of Newton's death there was no satisfactory critical account of his life and work.

[b] THE 250TH ANNIVERSARY OF THE
PUBLICATION OF THE PRINCIPIA, 1937:
CHERRY, T. A.: *Newton's Principia in 1687 and 1937*. Melbourne, 1937. A lecture in which special reference is made to the mathematical resources at Newton's disposal.

[c] THE 300TH ANNIVERSARY OF THE BIRTH OF
NEWTON, 1942:
THE ROYAL SOCIETY: *Newton Tercentenary Celebrations*, Cambridge, 1947. A collection of lectures delivered at meetings held in 1946 and attended by delegates from some thirty-five countries. On the title page, Sir Robert Robinson, President of the Royal Society writes: "The war prevented an international celebration in 1942 of the 300th anniversary of the birth of Isaac Newton. The Royal Society of London has taken this opportunity of inviting the national academies of science of the world to join with it in paying homage to his memory."

Some Recent Books

VILLAMIL DE, R.: *Newton: the Man*. London, 1931.

SULLIVAN, J. W. N.: *Isaac Newton*. London, 1938.

CRAIG, J.: *Newton at the Mint*. Cambridge, 1946.

MCLACHLAN, H.: *Sir Isaac Newton. Theological Manuscripts*. Liverpool, 1950.

ANDRADE, E. N. DA C.: *Isaac Newton*. London, 1950.

ANDRADE, E. N. DA C.: *Sir Isaac Newton*. London, 1954.

MOORE, PATRICK: *Isaac Newton*. London, 1957.

COHEN, I. BERNARD: *Franklin and Newton. An Inquiry into Speculative Newtonian Experimental Science and Franklin's Work in Electricity as an Example Thereof*. This volume, published by the American Philosophical Society, contains an extensive bibliography, which of course includes many references to Franklin. Philadelphia, 1956.

COHEN, I. BERNARD, assisted by Robert E. Schofield: *Isaac Newton's Papers and Letters on Natural Philosophy and related Documents*. Cambridge, 1958. A feature of the book is the facsimile reproduction of a great number of important documents.

TURNBULL, H. W.: *The Correspondence of Isaac Newton*. Volume I, 1661–1675, published for the Royal Society 1959. This volume, with others to follow, forms the only complete collection of Newton's correspondence. There are valuable notes by the Editor on individual letters. The publication of Newton's correspondence, at this time, aptly commemorates the 300th anniversary of the founding of the Royal Society in 1660.

This list includes certain words which have special meanings in the records of the Universities of the British Isles. It is based on the New English Dictionary, edited by J. A. H. Murray, Oxford University Press.

ALMA MATER (Latin *alma mater*—bounteous mother)—title given by Romans to several goddesses, especially to Ceres and Cybele. Universities and schools are regarded as "fostering mothers" to their *alumni* (Latin *alumnus*—a foster child, from *alere*—to nourish: *almus*—nourishing).

CHANCELLOR (Latin *cancellarius*—usher of a law-court who was stationed at the bar (*ad cancellos*) of a law-court). The titular head of a university; the actual duties are performed by a Vice-Chancellor. The word is also used in connection with other official offices, e.g. Lord Chancellor, Chancellor of the Exchequer, Chancellor of the Duchy of Lancaster, Chancellor of a Chapter of a Cathedral.

COLLEGE (Latin *collega*—colleague, from *col*—together, *legere* —to choose). Independent self-governing corporation or society of scholars, such as at Oxford and Cambridge, the College of the Sorbonne in Paris. Other uses include College of Cardinals, College of Arms.

DEAN (Latin *decanum*—one set over ten). The title of one or more resident Fellows, of an Oxford or Cambridge college, appointed to supervise conduct and studies of junior members. Wider uses include president of a faculty or department of study in a university. Also ecclesiastical usage as the head of the Chapter or body of canons of a collegiate or cathedral church.

FELLOW (Old English *feoh*—property or money and *lag*—to lay. The primary sense is one who lays down money in a joint undertaking with others). The name given to the incorporated members of a college or collegiate foundation. In colleges chiefly devoted to study and education the term Fellow was applied to senior scholars who had graduated or passed out of the stage of tutelage. Wider use includes titles given to members of learned societies.

MASTER (Latin *magister*, related to *magis*—more). The head or presiding officer of certain colleges, e.g. Master of Trinity College. The word is widely used in other contexts.

PROVOST (Anglo-French *provost*; Latin *praepositus* from *prae* —before, *ponere*—to place). A president or chief, and so, e.g. Provost of King's College, Cambridge. Also ecclesiastical and secular uses.

PRESIDENT (Latin *præsidere*—to preside). The title sometimes borne by the head of a College, e.g. President of Queens' College, Cambridge. Also ecclesiastical and secular uses.

SCHOOL (Latin *schola*—school from Greek σκολη —leisure). In medieval academic usage, the sphere or domain of academic discussion; thus in the plural, a building belonging to a university for lectures, disputations and academic meetings.

SCHOLAR (Latin *scholaris*—scholar). One who studies in the "schools" at a university and who receives emoluments as a reward of merit.

SENATE (Latin *senatus*—a council of old men). The official title of the governing body of some universities.

SIZAR—an undergraduate in the University of Cambridge or at Trinity College, Dublin, receiving an allowance from a college to enable him to study—probably receiving his "sizes" free (the "size" being a quantity or portion of bread, ale, etc.). Subsizar, ranking below a sizar.

TUTOR (Latin *tutor*—watcher, protector, from *tueri* to watch, guard). In the Universities of Oxford, Cambridge and Dublin, a graduate (usually a Fellow) to whom the special supervision of an undergraduate (called his pupil) is assigned. Hence the phrase *in statu pupillari* to denote the status of an undergraduate, and certain Bachelors (holders of a degree) of less than three and a half years' standing from their first degree.

VICE-CHANCELLOR (see Chancellor).

PRINTED IN GREAT BRITAIN BY
NORTHUMBERLAND PRESS LIMITED
GATESHEAD ON TYNE